THE LIFE OF SCIENCE

BOOKS IN
THE LIFE OF SCIENCE LIBRARY

THE LIFE OF SCIENCE
Essays in the History of Civilization
BY GEORGE SARTON

VICTORY OVER PAIN
A History of Anesthesia
BY VICTOR ROBINSON

BENJAMIN SILLIMAN
Pathfinder in American Science
BY JOHN F. FULTON and ELIZABETH H. THOMSON

SUN, STAND THOU STILL
The Life and Work of Copernicus the Astronomer
BY ANGUS ARMITAGE

THE LIFE
OF SCIENCE

Essays in the History of Civilization

BY GEORGE SARTON

Associate of the Carnegie Institution of Washington
Professor of the History of Science, Harvard University

FOREWORD BY MAX H. FISCH

 HENRY SCHUMAN · NEW YORK

FOREWORD

There is in the making a movement of thought toward a new focus in the history of science. Though interrupted by two world wars and a great depression, it has been steadily taking shape and gathering strength. It has drawn to itself a considerable number of our more thoughtful scientists, historians, and educators. So far, it has spoken the language of scholars. In *The Life of Science Library*, it is beginning to speak the language of lay men and women, girls and boys.

Among the scholars, George Sarton, who holds the chair of the History of Science at Harvard University, is respected and loved as the leader of the movement. It was he who conceived and fashioned its two basic tools: the *Introduction to the History of Science*, which he has now brought through the fourteenth century, and the journal *Isis*, with its systematic and critical bibliographies of current publications in the field.

Dr. Sarton has not only led in developing a sound scholarly basis for the movement, but he has been the most eloquent voice of its ideals as a new form of humanism which is needed to do for our time what an older humanism did for the Renaissance.

Many of the essays in which he has expressed these ideals can be read with understanding and enjoyment by the wider circle of readers for whom *The Life of Science Library* is intended. It has seemed to the publisher and sponsors of *The Life of Science Library* that its purposes could not be better conveyed than by gathering together in the present volume a selection from these essays.

The essays chosen, though far apart in time of composition, are united by spirit and intent. They were not planned with a view to being collected here. Yet, when read together, they have virtues a more formal treatment would lack. By their very diversity of subject and method, they give the beginner and the layman a livelier sense of the range of forms the history of science may take, and of the values that may be expected from it. They show by varied and lucid examples, both topical and biographical, that it is no narrow specialty but a liberating approach to human culture as a whole.

They are linked, moreover, by certain recurring themes: *The unity of mankind; The unity of knowledge; The international character of science; The kinship of artists, saints, and scientists as fulfillers of human destiny, as creators and diffusers of spiritual values; The history of art, religion, and science as the essential history of mankind, which has so far been largely "secret history"; Science as progressive in a way in which art and religion are not; The dependence of other forms of progress upon scientific progress; The history of science as, therefore, the leading thread in the history of civilization, the clue to the synthesis of knowledge, the mediator between science and philosophy, and the keystone of education.* The reader learns to recognize and welcome the variations on these themes. They end by becoming signposts for his own thinking.

Since reading these essays in proof, I have been turning over again the pages of the thirty-eight volumes of *Isis*, and re-reading Dr. Sarton's contributions to them—especially his prefaces. In an essay, "The Faith of a Humanist," which did duty in 1920 as preface in Volume III, he quoted a sentence from the classical scholar Gilbert Murray: "One might say roughly that material things are superseded but spiritual things not; or that everything considered as an achievement can be superseded, but considered as so much life, not." Dr. Sarton added:

It is true that most men of letters, and, I am sorry to add, not a few scientists, know science only by its material achievements, but ignore its spirit and see neither its internal beauty nor the beauty it extracts continually from the bosom of nature. Now I would say that to find in the works of science of the past, that which is not and cannot be superseded, is perhaps the most important part of our quest. A true humanist must know *the life of science* as he knows the life of art and the life of religion.

When I suggested to my friend Henry Schuman that the phrase I have italicized be used as title for the series in which this volume appears, I did not have this passage in mind, but it might well serve as a motto for the series.

University of Illinois   MAX H. FISCH

CONTENTS

PART ONE

THE SPREAD OF UNDERSTANDING

1. THE SPREAD OF UNDERSTANDING

"How impatient you are!" He pats my shoulder with his heavy hand while he repeats: "How impatient you are!" But his kind eyes belie the severity of his voice and he hastens to add, as if fearing that he had been too harsh: "Of course that is just as it should be. Though they have so much more time before them, we must expect the younger people—especially full-blooded ones—to be in more of a hurry, to be less patient. It would be a sadder world if the young were tolerant. Yet, listen to me. You say the world is out of joint. I have heard that before. Has it ever been otherwise? The tree-dwellers and the cave men, I am sure, had already denounced the out-of-jointedness of their own jungle. So put it that way, if you please, but I believe it is wiser to conceive mankind as an organism, as yet undeveloped but moving steadily from chaos to order. The progress is very slow but undeniable.

"And should we call it slow? How can we measure its speed? Think of it and you will realize that to speak of the slowness of evolution is nonsense. What we really mean is that our own span of life is very short. We can see but an absurdly small part of the play. How dare we criticise it, how dare we decide whether the action is slow or not? The great war was terrible enough, the wounds it made in millions of hearts may never be healed, but who can say how much of a scar it will leave on the fair face of the earth? It is considerably easier to destroy than to build. Why should we expect the reconstruction to be completed faster than the devastation? Why should we imagine that the world can be transformed—or improved, as you say—within our lifetime? Is that not foolish? . . . The world is not out of joint, my dear, but your telescope and your clock are out of order."

Uncle Christiaan is one of the most lovable old gentlemen

3

that the generous soil of Flanders has ever produced, but as
the years go by, he becomes ever more opinionated and more
tyrannical. Once he is well started, I know that my chances of
escaping are very small. As he had now made up his mind to
prove that I was wrong to expect the world to move as if its
own life were hardly longer than my own, I knew that he would
not let me go on until he had labored his argument at least ten
times over and I resigned myself meekly to my fate—for I love
Uncle Christiaan, even if he drives me mad. And then his knowledge and his wisdom are very great and it is worth while to
record at least the gist of what he said; but as he is hopelessly
discursive and as I could not possibly reproduce the saving humor of his tone, and his smiles and gestures, it will be best
to tell the story in my own way. Not one story, but *three* stories,
for the old man is nothing if not thorough. As a matter of fact
he told me *seven,* and he would have told as many more but
that I admitted he was right and promised that I would be more
patient in the future.

The First Story. One of the greatest discoveries man ever made
is that of our numerals, but we are so familiar with them that
we take them too much for granted. Yet if you begin to think
it over, is that system not very admirable which enables us
not simply to write down any number very quickly and without ambiguity, but also to use those numbers in our computations, to manipulate them according to a few fixed rules for
any length of time, almost mechanically, and to obtain finally
another number, written in the same short-hand, and representing the very result which we had started to find out?

To be sure, we might have obtained the same result by counting with pebbles, but that would have consumed far more time.
It would have been on the whole more difficult, our chances of
error greater and the errors themselves harder to detect.

Our system of numerals is not so simple as it seems to be,
for it involves at least three distinct ideas. To consider first the

most conspicuous but the least important of them, we use only ten symbols to write any number. That is, our system is decimal. The beauty of this is that the number of figures is so small. It might have been smaller still—a system of eight figures would have done very well—or else, a little larger—twelve would have made an ideal set—but not much larger without sensibly increasing the difficulty of computations. For in the case of a duodecimal system, our children would have to learn by rote their table of multiplication up to 12, and so on. Why did we choose ten? The reason is simply that our ancestors made their family accounts on their fingers or on their toes, and they happened to be, just like ourselves, ten-fingered and ten-toed. Ten thus became naturally the basis of their numeration. It is true that some other people developed other systems: the Babylonians used the basis sixty and the Mayas—most intelligent of the original Americans—the basis twenty. However, the basis ten is now almost universally used, at least as far as the numbers themselves are concerned.

The second idea is what we now call the principle of local value. That is the very heart of this immense discovery. When we write 324, for example, we mean to represent a collection constituted by 4 units, plus 2 tens, plus 3 hundreds. We know at once that the 3 stands for hundreds, for it is written at the third place from the right; if it were written at the seventh place, it would mean 3 millions.

The third idea is, so to say, an elaboration of the second: what would one do if there were no units of a certain order? How should we write three millions and four hundreds, for example? One might leave an open space between the 4 and the 3, and another between the 3 and a final dot, but that would be very ambiguous. Some unknown genius (or, maybe, many) hit upon the device of creating a special symbol, the zero, representing no number, but to be used only to mark that units of a certain order were missing. Thus if we write 3,000,400 there can be no misunderstanding. A careful definition of the new symbol enabled us to use it exactly as the older ones, without further ado. It seems that the Mayas knew the use of it, but they did not think of the decimal system. When, then, did the latter, that is, the combination of the three ideas, originate?

It is very probable that it originated in India sometime about the fifth or sixth century, if not earlier. The system was already known in Western Syria about 662. The Moslems who transmitted Greek, Hindu and Iranian knowledge to the Christian West introduced also the new numerals (which are often called Arabic numerals because of that). Yet it took the West a very long time to understand and to assimilate them. The earliest coin bearing the Hindu numerals is one with an Arabic legend struck in 1138 to commemorate the reign of Roger of Sicily. But the conditions obtaining in Sicily, where Byzantines, Latins and Moslems met on an equal footing, were too exceptional to be representative of Western Europe. However, by the end of the twelfth century a small élite was apparently familiar with the new system. Their formal and final introduction was due to Leonardo of Pisa, who published in 1202 a book containing a very clear explanation of the Hindu numerals and of the best ways of using them.

Mind you, more than six centuries had already passed since this discovery and as far as Europe was concerned, this was only the beginning, the first satisfactory and successful introduction of the subject. At the close of the thirteenth century the bankers of Florence were *forbidden* to use these numerals and we may gather that they actually used them, but in the face of a strong opposition. The only alternative was the clumsy Roman notation which offered a means of writing numbers in a manner unequivocal but very unclear; it was altogether out of the question to use them for any but the very simplest reckonings. One might say that the Roman numerals could be used solely because they were not used: all calculations were actually made by some kind of abacus or calculating table, and only the results, partial or final, were put down in Roman letters, the calculations themselves were lost in the sand or vanished with the motions of the counters.

The heroic period was now long over and the rest of the history of our numerals is but one example, among so many others, of the difficulty of overcoming the enormous inertia of vested traditions. The case is interesting because the new decimal system was a time- and labor-saving invention of the first magnitude.

The Hindus had made to mankind a gift of inestimable value. No strings of any kind were attached to it, nor was the suggested improvement entangled with any sort of religious or philosophic ideas. Those proposing to use the new numerals were not expected to make any disavowal or concession; nor could their feelings be hurt in any way. They were asked simply to exchange a bad tool for a good one. Yet it was not until the fourteenth and fifteenth centuries that the new system was generally accepted in Italy, and not until the sixteenth and even the beginning of the seventeenth that it was finally established in the rest of civilized Europe.

All counted, more than a millennium had elapsed between the discovery and its general acceptance, even in that primary stage. In the meanwhile, it is true, the center of civilization had moved from Southern Asia to Western Europe, but that had not been the cause of the delay. Mountains and seas and even desert plains are smaller obstacles to the diffusion of ideas than the unreasonable obstinacy of man. The main barriers to overcome are not outside, but inside the brain.

The Second Story (which is very different, and yet not so different). It is well known that the circulation of the blood in the human body was satisfactorily explained for the first time by William Harvey. The first idea of this discovery occurred to him not later than 1616 but he did not publish it until 1628 in a little book dealing with the motion of the heart and blood. One is rather surprised to find that this book did not make more stir; neither did it arouse much opposition, at least in England. In France the opposition to the new theory was considerable, but even there, and bitter as it was, it did not last very long. More happy in this than many other forerunners, Harvey was granted a taste of victory before his death in 1657. By 1673 his cause was definitely won, even in France, and the people who had been his contemporaries could witness the complete supremacy of the new doctrine.

Thus less than half a century had been needed to ensure its triumph. The speed of this reception is less wonderful, however, than the lateness of the discovery itself, for as to Harvey's priority there can be no doubt. How is it then that no one anticipated him? There was nothing whatever in the nature of this discovery—as Harvey made it—to prevent its being made many centuries before: nothing but prejudice.

Until the time of Harvey, the prevalent conception was that promulgated by Galen, more than fourteen centuries earlier. It is not easy at all to give a complete account of Galen's ideas, but it will suffice to note the following points. According to him, the blood was produced in the liver from the materials furnished by our food and was then transported to the right half of the heart. Some of it passed into the left half, where it was imbued with new properties, and became fit to nourish the whole body. To use Galenic language, the blood of the right heart was endowed with "natural spirits," that of the left heart with "vital spirits." The latter blood was thus essentially different from the former. They did not circulate in the body, but both moved in a ceaseless ebb and flow, each in its own domain. But how did the blood pass from the right to the left ventricle? To explain the impossible, Galen had been obliged to assume that it passed through innumerable *invisible* pores in the solid wall which divides the right heart from the left. Nobody ever detected these pores for they are not simply invisible but nonexistent. Yet Galen, supreme pontiff of Greek medicine, and nine centuries later Avicenna, the infallible medical pope of the middle ages, had spoken *ex cathedra* with such indisputable authority that this gratuitous assumption was generally taken for gospel.

Even a man like Leonardo da Vinci, endowed with so much genius and originality, and who had himself dissected a large number of bodies and examined very minutely many a heart, even he was subjugated by this intangible dogma. This is the more pathetic in that Leonardo was certainly on the scent of the true explanation, but the invisible holes were too sacred to be touched, and nothing but this prejudice caused his failure to discover and to proclaim the circulation of the blood.

When I shut my eyes and evoke the past, I imagine that this great discovery was enclosed in a chest of which intelligent observers like Leonardo, Vesalius, Servetus or Columbus could have easily found the secret if they had set their hearts upon it, but they did not dare approach near enough because Prejudice sat on the lid. I can see those great men standing shyly around the coffer, mysteriously attracted by it, yet awed into impotence, while Truth was prisoner inside.

A moment of reflection will now convince you that the second story is not so widely different from the first as it might appear at first view. In both cases the application of a great discovery was delayed for more than a millennium by unreasonable prejudices. But in the first case the obstruction occurred after the discovery and prevented it from becoming effective, while in the second, prejudice blocked the way to the discovery itself, preventing it from being made.

The Third Story (which is in some way a sequel to the first). Prince Maurice of Nassau, stathouder of the Low Countries, took into his service about the year 1593 a Fleming of considerable genius, Simon Stevin of Bruges. He used to refer to him for mathematical advice and employed him as his chief hydraulic engineer and as quartermaster general of his armies. This Stevin has not yet received his full meed of recognition, for he certainly was one of the greatest men of the sixteenth century. Various important discoveries or inventions are ascribed to him and the historian of mechanics can quote no greater name for the whole interval (of more than eighteen centuries) between Archimedes and Galileo. In the year 1585 Stevin published, in both a Dutch and French edition, a little booklet entitled *The Tithe*, wherein he gave for the first time a systematic account of decimal fractions. Though he was not the first to think of such fractions, he showed such a deep understanding and gave such a masterly exposition of them, that we will not be far wrong if we call him their inventor. His manner of representing them was rather clumsy, however, and that might have delayed their diffusion, had this brilliant innovation not been reinforced a little later by another invention at least equally important, that of the logarithms. The logarithms, like the decimals, made it possible to increase considerably the speed of computation. It has been justly said that the discovery of logarithms doubled the lives of the astronomers. They were introduced at the beginning of the following century (1614, 1619) by John Napier, laird of Merchiston, who showed us at the same time a far simpler method of representing the decimal fractions, the very one we use today. The triumph of the logarithms was immediate—no amount of prejudice could have prevented the astronomers from doubling their years!—and the decimals shared the triumph as a matter of course. But here again our surprise is not that these fractions were accepted so readily, but that they were offered so late.

Indeed what did they stand for? Just as the main idea of the decimal system was to collect the objects to be counted in tens, tens of tens, or hundreds, and so on; so the gist of the decimal fractions was to count fragments of unity similarly in tenths, tenths of tenths or hundredths, etc. When this was consistently done it was found that those fractions could be written and used almost as simply as ordinary numbers. The decimal fractions, so to say, drove the fractions out of our calculations and the more so that one could always suppress them altogether if one wished. If it annoyed you too much to speak of $3.53, you could say, without changing a single figure, 353 cents. The decimal fractions are so simple that most people handle them without being aware of their presence, just as Monsieur Jourdain spoke in prose, without his knowing it.

The most convincing proof of Stevin's genius was perhaps that after having explained the decimal fractions, he did not rest there. He saw at once the logical consequences of their introduction and the immense possibilities which were involved. Decimal numbers are naturally introduced when we enumerate objects if we count them by tens, but what will happen if our numbers are the result not of a direct enumeration, but of a mensuration—as when we want to know the length of a piece of cloth or the weight of a cheese? Then it is clear that we can only obtain the same fractions that are included in our instruments. Thus if we deal with feet and inches or shillings and pence we are driven to use duodecimal fractions which do not at all tally with our decimal system. Stevin was the first to realize that the adoption of a decimal system of numbers led irresistibly to that of a decimal system of weights and measures (and *vice versa*) and that neither adoption was truly complete without the other. To measure according to one system and to count according to another destroyed the economy of both.

This great vision of Stevin's was beautifully simple, as simple as it was deep, yet it was not embodied until the end of the eighteenth century, when the French Revolution created the so-called metric system. The idea was accepted by the *Assemblée Constituante* in 1790 and the system became legally established in France. During the last century it spread all over the world, except, strangely enough, in the Anglo-Saxon countries where it met—and still meets—with a resistance, which is the stronger in that it is irrational. In the fifteenth century, there were still any number of learned doctors and professors who claimed that the Roman letters were much clearer than the Hindu numerals. Was it not much simpler to write CCCXLVIII than 348? In the same way, there are still many English and American apostles, full of learning, who will prove to everybody who will listen that their incongruous sets of weights, measures and moneys are much more convenient than the metric system! How can they do it? I really don't know, but they do it with a fervor only equalled by the paradoxical absurdity of their plea. A Frenchman needs no fraction but the decimal,* and these can take care of themselves, so to say; he hardly notices them. On the contrary your Englishman uses vigesimal fractions if he speaks of pounds sterling and shillings; both Americans and Englishmen need duodecimal fractions when dealing with feet and inches, and sixteenths to measure in pounds avoirdupois and ounces, and many more varieties each of which seems to be entirely independent of the others. The factor ten is about the only one absent from his tables of weights and measures, yet he clings faithfully to the decimal system of numbers! It looks as if after having admitted the superiority of these numbers, his need of order had been exhausted and he stopped short, discouraged, on the road of improvement.

When Uncle Christiaan had reached this point of the story—the story which he was telling in order to instil into my soul the noble virtue of patience—he became so enraged that he could hardly master his feelings or choose his words: "Think of it! Try to visualize this great discovery made in India about the sixth century, perfected in the Low Countries in the sixteenth, completed in France at the end of the eighteenth: one of the greatest labor-saving discoveries which the human race has ever made. Can you imagine that the nations which are in many respects the most civilized of our own times have not yet grasped its importance? The work of more than ten generations has not sufficed to convince them with regard to a truth of the simplest and most objective kind!

"It makes me mad to think of the time which the children must need to become familiar with those grotesque assortments of weights and measures. As if they were not yet sufficiently handi-

---

* Except when measuring time and angles, when he uses sexagesimal fractions, because the Babylonians wore such a deep rut with respect to these, some four thousand years ago, that mankind has not yet been able to extricate itself from it.

capped by the most erratic spelling of all languages dead or alive. Poor children! It did not matter so much in the past, when they had but little to learn, but now that we can not find enough time to teach them the essentials, it seems almost criminal to waste their attention upon such artificial knowledge. For even if they should know all the relations between those measures, and all the eccentricities of the English dictionary, and even, if you please, the peculiarities of many other languages, would they be able to understand the world any better? Certainly not. They might just as well have memorized the telephone directory. For example, to know that you must spell *knee* and pronounce *nee* is no real knowledge for it does not teach you anything about the nature of things in general or of knees in particular. This gives one at best a clearer notion of human perversity; it can give one no knowledge of nature, no understanding of the cosmos. Poor little children, victims of the insane obstinacy of their elders and of the ignorance and lack of imagination of the educators. . . ."

Uncle Christiaan is so overcome that he will not talk any more. It is my turn now to soothe and humor him. Soon he will recover his enthusiasm and, maybe, his voice.

To be sure, in the domain of pure science, progress has now become far more rapid because the value of discoveries is no longer judged by the crowds from an irrational point of view, but by experts from a purely technical one. Even the most revolutionary theories, such as radioactivity, the quanta, or relativity, are examined quietly by a very small body of scientists who are kept constantly on their guard by mutual criticism and who are expected to justify their every opinion. Their verdict, whichever it be, destroys any irrational obstruction in the egg. Unfortunately such improved methods can be used only in the case of problems amenable to a scientific treatment, without any philosophic or sentimental loophole, and which are of sufficient technicality to be beyond the reach of meddling people. In the field of technology, though so close to that of science, new ideas may be jeopardized or their success considerably delayed, by various irrelevant circumstances. This explains why the proper launching of an invention is so tremendously important. But when it comes to social or political problems (not to speak of religious ones) it is almost as difficult to obtain a proper appreciation of them as it was in the middle ages. Indeed a large number of the non- or half-educated people, even of the most enlightened nations, are still intellectually in the medieval stage. That is, they are uncritical, unable to judge matters dispassionately, unable to disentangle truth from its web of prejudice. We should not, in our turn, judge them too severely, for even the greatest heroes of truth were not entirely untrammelled. It humbles our minds but mollifies our hearts to realize that each of them, after having fought gallantly, one after another, the errors and the prejudices which lay ambushed along his way, was finally checked by some imaginary obstacle which he could not overcome, by a last prepossession which he durst not challenge.

2. THE HISTORY OF MEDICINE VERSUS THE HISTORY OF ART *

IN REMEMBRANCE OF FIELDING H. GARRISON

I

I appreciate the honor of having been invited to deliver this lecture, and I welcome the opportunity of paying homage to the memory of an old friend, who was a distinguished historian and did perhaps more than anybody else to promote the cultivation of the history of medicine in our country. There is no medical or reference library, however small, without a copy of one of the editions of his *Introduction to the History of Medicine*, and many American doctors have derived their knowledge of the subject almost exclusively from it. They were fortunate in having such a good source of information, for Garrison's *Introduction* is, all considered, the best one-volume account of the medical past, especially the more recent past which concerns more immediately our contemporaries.

II

The subject of my lecture was selected on two grounds. Firstly, it enabled me to reassess the views formulated in the essay introducing *Isis* ‡ (1912); and secondly, it was a means of showing the humanity of Garrison's history. In spite of the lack of space (for the evocation of the whole medical past in less than a thousand pages is somewhat of an adventure), Garrison always man-

---

* The Fielding H. Garrison Lecture, read at the Seventeenth Annual Meeting of the American Association of the History of Medicine, May 1941.

‡ An international journal devoted to the history of science, the official quarterly organ of the History of Science Society.

aged to add the human touch without which history remains hopelessly dull. He thus illustrated his own sensitiveness to the essential if elusive values without which our life has no savor and
hardly deserves to be recorded.

He was especially sensitive to music: witness his many references to it. These references were of necessity very brief, but I
shall expand two of them in order to bring forth their rich implications.

I have the reputation of being a hard worker and among the
physicians listening to me to-day are perhaps many who work as
hard as I do, or harder still; yet, as compared with the famous
Dutch physician, Hermann Boerhaave, we are but self-indulging
weaklings. According to his early biographer, William Burton,

> The mornings and evenings he devoted to study, the intermediate
> part of the day to domestic and public affairs. He used to rise
> during summer at four in the morning, and at five in the winter,
> even in his later years; ten was his usual bed time. In severest win-
> ters he had neither fire nor stove in his study, where he passed the
> three or four first hours of the morning: his application to study
> was greater in the last ten years of his life, than in any space of
> equal duration from the year 1700. When business was over, he
> took the exercise of riding or walking, and when weary revived
> himself with music, his most delightful entertainment; being not
> only a good performer on several instruments, particularly the
> lute, which he accompanied also with his voice, but a good
> theorist likewise in the science, having read the ancient and best
> modern authors on the subject, as appears by the lectures he
> gave on sound and hearing; and during the winter he had once
> a week a concert at his own house, to which by turns were in-
> vited some select acquaintance of both sexes, and likewise pa-
> tients of distinction from other countries.

His teaching should presumably be understood as a part of
those "domestic and public affairs" which occupied the inter-
mediate part of his day. Perhaps he thought, as many scholars do,
that teaching was not real work but rather an interruption of it.

And yet he taught a lot, not only clinical medicine and ophthalmology (in 1708, he gave the first special course on that subject), but also physics, chemistry and botany! In those days, famous professors did not occupy a chair but a whole settee.

Boerhaave's musical interest must have been deep, for he devoted a special section to it in his autobiography. That section (XXII) is very brief (seven words), but that is of a piece with the rest. Boerhaave was too busy a man down to his last day to indulge in reminiscences. Here it is:

> XXII. Fessus testudinis concentu solabatur lassitudinem. Musices amantissimus.

How eloquent are those few words! Since I have read them and pondered upon them, Boerhaave is more alive to me than he was before, and I can almost see him with his "testudo" (not a tortoise that, but a lute) relaxing his mind when his duty was done.

III

The other story concerns Theodor Billroth (1829-94), one of the greatest surgeons of his time; the pioneer of visceral surgery. Whatever be his greatness or his shortcomings as a surgeon, we shall love him better if we realize that he was a life-long friend of Johannes Brahms (1833-97). Brahms and he became very intimate in Zürich, and when Billroth was called to Vienna, Brahms, being a bachelor and without position, followed him there. Though they spent much of their time together and often travelled together, they exchanged a great many letters, of which 331 are preserved. These letters deal chiefly with musical matters, most of Brahms' works being discussed in a friendly fashion. The surgeon's villa in Alsergrund (a suburb of Vienna) became a musical center. Indeed, he enjoyed the *jus primae noctis* over Brahms' new creations, and the friends of both masters were given opportunities of hearing for the first time some of the masterpieces of chamber music. Did they appreciate their privilege? Probably not. But we are interested here primarily in the relationship between the composer and the doctor,—a relationship which is, I believe, unique in its intensity. Billroth was a good amateur, a clever pianist and a capable viola player much in demand for quartets (bless the gentle violists for we need them). Under the combined influence of his scientific studies and of Brahms' conversations, Billroth devoted more and more thought to the psychophysiological basis of music and gathered a number of notes on the subject which were edited after his death under the title "Wer ist musikalisch?" by no less a person than Eduard Hanslick (1825-1904). Who remembers Hanslick to-day? Yet he was the leading critic of the German world, pontificating for a third of a century in the *Neue freie Presse*, defending with painful iteration the canons of "musical beauty" and of the "significant form" (*beseelte Form*). He was a member of the *Brahmsgemeinde* (Brahms clique) and was the champion of the Schumanns, of Brahms, of Dvořák against the *Musik der Zukunft*. If Liszt and Wagner irritated him so much what would he have thought, I wonder, of the musical anarchists of our own days, of the "jazz" and "swing," of all the music which seems to be written for the spinal cord rather than for the brain? At that time the arch-offender was Wagner, and I sometimes ask myself whether Hanslick was not right in his distrust of the Wagnerian witchery? Historians discussing our times a few centuries hence will be able to discern more clearly than we can the spiritual origins of the present chaos. They will probably recognize Wagner and Nietzsche as the leaders in the movement to pull Germany back to the *Nibelungen* level.

IV

There is considerably more to be said about medicine and music, but these two examples must suffice. It is more pleasant to talk about that, I think, than to write, for the talking would be less deliberate and we could digress more capriciously, and perhaps stop talking, to listen to music. For what is the good of talking about music? Let us listen. Take the *Third piano quartet in C minor* (op. 60). When Brahms sent the finished work to Billroth in 1874 he wrote: "I am showing you the quartet purely as a curiosity! An illustration as it were, to the last chapter of the man in a blue swallow tail and yellow waistcoat. . . ." Or take the two *Rhapsodies for piano*, dedicated to Frau Elisabeth von Herzogenberg (op. 19, c. 1878). Listen, and remember Billroth's comment: "In these two pieces there lingers more of the titanic young Brahms than in the last works of his maturity." Without the music itself, either present or remembered, these words are meaningless, and there is no point in quoting more.

Let us return to the history of medicine. I am afraid that many physicians think of it too much in terms of a list of discoveries and achievements. In fact, such lists have been compiled in such a dry and impersonal manner that the names of physicians associated with each "item" might almost be replaced by an x, y, or z. Such lists are useful, but they are to the history of medicine hardly more than a skeleton is to a living body. The skeleton is indispensable to be sure, but insufficient.

A mere list of discoveries is a falsification of the history of medicine, even from the purely scientific point of view, for such a list exaggerates the discontinuities in medical progress. A deeper study of almost any discovery reveals that what we call the discovery is only the final clinching of an argument developed by many men throughout a long period of time. However, such a list is a far greater falsification from the broad human point of view.

The history of science, and in particular the history of medicine (we can not repeat it too often) is not simply an account of discoveries. Its purpose is to explain the development of the scientific spirit, the history of man's reactions to truth, the history of the gradual revelation of truth, the history of the gradual liberation of our minds from darkness and prejudice. Discoveries are evanescent, for they are soon replaced by better ones. The historian must try not only to describe these evanescent discoveries but to find in science that which is timeless. When he does that he comes very close to the historian of art. To put it in other words, a man's name may be immortalized by his discoveries. Perhaps there was nothing else in him deserving of remembrance? He may have been a poor sort of man, a man whose mind was as sharp and narrow as a knife-edge? Or else the historian betrayed him? In so far as a scientist is also an artist, his personality can survive, otherwise not. It is the historian's main duty to revive the personalities, rather than to enumerate their scientific excrescences. Discoveries may be important, but personalities are infinitely more so.

V

The materials investigated by historians of art often are of great value to historians of medicine, because artistic traditions are likely to be more tangible than purely scientific ones. This is especially true of ancient and mediaeval times, during which the diffusion of knowledge was necessarily difficult and erratic. Beautiful monuments had on the whole a better chance of survival than others, and their language is easier to understand, even to-day. Dr. Sigerist has given remarkable examples of the mutual aid of the history of medicine and the history of art in his lecture, "The historical aspect of art and medicine." Remember his pictorial history of the plague, and his account of the transformation of Apollo into St. Sebastian, both being saviors or intercessors in times of pestilence.

Such examples might easily be multiplied and a balanced explanation of them would enrich, as well as fortify, our traditions. I have adumbrated some of them in the first volume of *Isis*— apropos of the history of cultivated plants—and in my *Introduction to the History of Science*, e.g., indicating the importance of the pilgrimage roads, such as the Way of St. James (to Santiago

 mention of the mystery brings us close to the heart of our
⬛t, for it is there on its threshold that art and knowledge and
⬛neet and kneel together. This will appear more clearly when
⬛ve examined how far art and science diverge in the ordinary
⬛e of life. After having completed that examination, briefly
⬛ must, we shall retrace our steps and peep once more into the
⬛uary.

⬛e outstanding difference between art and science is that the
⬛ is progressive while the former is not. Scientific activities
⬛he only ones which are cumulative and progressive. Thus
⬛ng the history of science gives us the exhilarating feeling of
⬛ing a mountain; we may go downward sometime for a short
⬛ or we may turn around its slopes, but the general direction is
⬛ard, and the top of the mountain is lost in the clouds. Every
⬛itist is enabled to start off from the highest level reached by
⬛predecessors, and if he have it in him, to go higher still. The
⬛ory of art, on the contrary, is like a glacial landscape, a plain
⬛rein many hills are unevenly scattered. You may climb one of
⬛se hills and reach the summit,—but then you cannot continue
⬛hout going down to the level land; then up again, and so on.
⬛When I began my ascension of the topless mountain, I used to
⬛t over that. Progress, here it was indeed and nowhere else.
⬛fortunately, there is the devil to pay for it. Because of the pro-
⬛ssive nature of science, its achievements are evanescent. Each
⬛ is bound to be superseded, sooner or later, by a better one
⬛ then it loses its practical value and becomes like a neglected
⬛l in a museum showcase. On the other hand, because of art's
⬛y unprogressiveness, works of art are eternally young. It is very
⬛ficult to read an old scientific treatise, for in order to under-
⬛nd it properly, one must know equally well the old science and
⬛ new, and everything before and between. It is painful to read
⬛ewton, but the plays of Shakespeare are as timely and pleasur-
⬛le to-day as they ever were. "A thing of beauty is a joy forever."

de Compostela), and of the dispersion of Romanesque and Gothic
architecture.

Much as they are needed for the following up of Western traditions, they are needed considerably more for the understanding of
Eastern ones. Indeed, Western traditions are supported by literary
witnesses in Greek, Latin or vernaculars which offer no special
difficulties; while the Eastern literatures are generally closed to all
but a few Orientalists, and the latter's knowledge is almost always
restricted to a single group of languages. Now consider this case.
In the beginning of the fourteenth century, a most remarkable culture was developed in Tabrîz under the patronage of the Mongol
rulers of Persia. The spiritual leader was Rashîd al-dîn, physician,
theologian and one of the outstanding historians of the Middle
Ages. He wrote chiefly in Persian, but had a deep knowledge of
Arabic and was acquainted (directly or through secretaries) with
documents written in Hebrew, Uighûr, Mongolian and Chinese.
A scientific edition of his works requires a good knowledge of all
of those languages. This you will admit is a big order. Happily, the
cosmopolitanism of that age and place can be perceived almost
immediately by any person sensitive to artistic values and knowing sufficiently the peculiarities of Asiatic arts. Indeed, under the
patronage of the same Rashîd al-dîn, there blossomed in Tabrîz a
school of miniaturists whose works reveal immediately the same
Chinese influences which can only be detected in the text by that
rara avis, an Orientalist as familiar with Chinese as with Persian
and Arabic. Indeed Chinese traits are just as obvious in those
fourteenth-century miniatures, as they were to become four centuries later in the ubiquitous "chinoiseries" which delighted our
rococo ancestors.

VI

The view that we need art for the understanding of science and
vice versa is by no means a new one, but it is so often forgotten or
obscured by good scientists and by good historians that it is neces-

sary to give it from time to time new strength and new life, and to treat it as if it were a novelty, the most important novelty of our own time. Among the best exponents of it in the last century, was a man who was also one of the pioneers of our own studies. Can you guess whom I mean? I will help you. He should not be difficult to find, for he was, a hundred years ago, the most famous man in the world. He is not so famous now, for the wheel of fortune never stops turning, even after one's death. He is a bit forgotten, and when our schoolboys are asked to name the most prominent men, no one would think of choosing him. After having received a scientific preparation which was as elaborate as it was diversified, and having crowned it with a literary initiation in the Weimar circle (Goethe, so critical of others, never wavered in his admiration of him), he spent five years exploring South America, then thirty more discussing and publishing the results of his observations. At the age of fifty-eight he delivered in Berlin a series of lectures which were but the sketch of the grand fresco of which he began the publication eighteen years later and to which he devoted the remainder of his life.

That man is—need I name him—Alexander von Humboldt, and the work of his old age to which I referred is the *Cosmos*. The first two volumes appeared in 1845 and 1847 (when he was 76 and 78), vols. 3 and 4 between 1850 and 1858; he died in 1859 at the age of 90, and volume 5 appeared three years later. We need consider only the first two volumes. The first contains an elaborate description and explanation of the physical world, and the second is a history of science. Thus Humboldt was a pioneer in geographical synthesis, and also in historical synthesis. He was a founder of the new geography and also of the new history. The first innovation was rapidly understood and was developed in many countries; the second was comparatively neglected. Geography and history are two necessary bases of a man's education; just as some knowledge of geography removes his provincialism with regard to space—that is, teaches him that things are not necessarily better in his own village, in his own metropolis or in

his own country than elsewhere—even so,
is the only way of removing his provinciali
—that is, of making him realize that thin
better in his days than in earlier or, maybe
geography nor history was new in Humbo
creased considerably the scope and the imp
example, he showed that history should be f
tory of science, and also upon the history o
most remarkable of all was his realization c
and sciences. After having described nature
Cosmos, he devoted the second volume to
nature as reflected in the human mind, by t
is art) or by the reasoning power (that is scie
he was breaking ground so new that the vast
and scholars of to-day have not yet grasped
to do.

The project was so ambitious that realizatio
but we must not blame him. Pioneers are beg
be expected to complete their task; it is not *the*
plete it. Some day the substance of that s
have to be worked out again and rewritten, bu
of unusual learning, artistry and wisdom to do
now, the great story which cries to be told is tha
the mutual interrelations between science, art
story is very difficult to tell, because it is not a
like the history of science, but of vacillations a
harmony followed by chaos, and beauty mixe
would be the story of man's sensitiveness to
problems and the main values of life.

All honor to Alexander von Humboldt for h
way, and the more so that we are so slow in follo
our scientists, so intelligent in some respects,
others, and our artists, so clever, yet so blind. Be
all to see, and truth, and virtue, but how few real
but different aspects of the same mystery?

VII

Th
subje
faith
we h
routi
as w
sanc

T
latte
are
read
clim
run
upv
scie
his
his
wh
tho
wit

gl
U
gr
or
ar
to
ve
d
s
tl
N
a

The following remarks made by Picasso in 1923 throw a curious light on this. Said he,

> To me there is no past or future in art. If a work of art cannot live always in the present it must not be considered at all. The art of the Greeks, of the Egyptians, of the great painters who lived in other times, is not an art of the past; perhaps it is more alive today than it ever was. Art does not evolve by itself, the ideas of people change and with them their mode of expression. When I hear people speak of the evolution of an artist, it seems to me that they are considering him standing between two mirrors that face each other and reproduce his image an infinite number of times, and that they contemplate the successive images of one mirror as his past, and the images of the other mirror as his future, while his real image is taken as his present. They do not consider that they all are the same images in different planes.*

Science is progressive and therefore ephemeral; art is non-progressive and eternal. A deeper contrast could not be imagined.

In the field of science, the methods are supremely important. A history of science is to a large extent a history of the instruments, material or immaterial, created by a succession of men to solve their several problems. Each instrument or each method is, as it were, a crystallization of human genius. Look at the cockpit of an airplane, and ask yourself what was the origin and development of each one of its tools; it is an endless story of patient accumulation and adjustment. In art, on the contrary, the results matter more than the methods. I am not interested in knowing how a symphony was produced, how a fresco was painted, how a dish was cooked. The beauty of the symphony and the painting satisfy me, and so does the tastiness of the food; I do not ask for the recipe.

The scientist strives to be more and more objective and accurate; the artist lets himself go and his accuracy is intangible. The

---

* *Picasso, forty years of his art*, 2nd ed., edited by Alfred H. Barr, Jr., issued by Museum of Modern Art (New York, 1939, p. 11).

scientist says: "If you can measure the thing, you are beginning
to know something about it, if not . . . ," but the artist answers,
"What about beauty and love?"

Science is essentially international, or perhaps we should say
supernational. Men of science of all times and places coöperate
together; they cannot help coöperating, even if they don't particularly wish to do so, because their task is essentially the same. They
are ascending the same mountain, and even when their trails diverge they are aiming at the same goal. Art is tribal, national. To
be sure, it may transcend local peculiarities and reach the bed-
rock of human nature. Yet when we speak of Spanish painting or
Russian music we evoke fundamental differences, which may be
difficult to analyze, not to say measure, but are as tangible as the
air we breathe. Sometime ago I had to write a study on Borodin,
who was a distinguished chemist as well as one of the leading
Russian composers. In order to reconstruct his background, I had
to investigate the contemporary state of *international* chemistry
and of *Russian* music.

The scientific procedure is essentially analytic; the artistic one
synthetic, intuitive. Scientific discoveries are the result of long
evolutions, artistic achievements of short involutions. This applies
not only to the creation of scientific or artistic works, but also to
their interpretation. We cannot penetrate the thought of Faraday
or Poincaré without a sustained effort, but a Greek statue reveals
to us immediately the best of Greece, and a Gothic cathedral il-
luminates the Middle Ages. Science is the field of arduous and
unremitting work; how beautiful the flowers in it are if we have
earned them with honest travail of limbs or spirit! Art, by contrast, is the paradise of immediate intuitions.

VIII

All of which is very true, but it is not the whole truth, and I
knew it all the time. Now let us look together at the other side of
the picture.

In science as in art, there is always a fundamental need of selection. Just as an artist cannot paint every landscape, or a lover love every woman, just so the scientist cannot investigate every problem. None of them has a ghost of a chance unless he restricts his goal. The immense success of science is due largely to the selection of problems, one at a time, the simplest and easiest first, and so on. Genius in science as well as in art is essentially the ability to select properly.

Then, too, there *is* technical progress in art. The history of music, like the history of science, can be written partly in terms of instruments. The modern symphony is as much an instrumental triumph as the transatlantic flights. Scientific knowledge is not simply rational, a good part of it is manual and intuitive. What a gulf there is between the born diagnostician and the physician who has learning enough but lacks insight! There is uncanny wisdom in the hands of a surgeon as well as in those of a pianist.

Science and art have both their collectivist aspects, as well as their individualist ones. The former are seen at their best in religious art and in social medicine, and that rapprochement is suggestive. For what is religious art, but the highest form of the social art? And what else is social medicine but the finest realization of the second commandment: "Thou shalt love thy neighbor as thyself"? Neither religious art nor social medicine can succeed unless they be sustained by a living faith.

Science, every science and of course medicine above all, is an art as soon as it is applied. It becomes part and parcel of a man's religion as soon as he is thoroughly conscious of his own insignificance and of his solidarity with the rest of the universe. We cannot understand the history of medicine, unless we see in it not only discoveries and scientific achievements, but also personal defeats and victories, the timeless fruits of men's love and faith. On the other hand, as Canon Streeter has remarked: "Science is the great cleanser of the human spirit, it makes impossible any religion but the highest." The well-tempered historian will keep this in mind always, and think of men's art and religion, as well as of their learning. He will try to see the whole of their personalities and thus give to his own work its greatest value for other men. Science is the reason, art the joy, religion the harmony, of life. None is complete without the others. We cannot hope to understand the mystery of life unless we be prepared to consider it from these three angles, and this means, first of all, that we must drop our scientific conceit, and second, that we must never, never, subordinate humanities to technicalities.

3. THE HISTORY OF SCIENCE

The history of science is the study of the development of science, —just as one studies the development of a plant or an animal— from its very birth. We try to see it grow and unfold itself under many diverse conditions. And it is not enough—as we shall see further on—to study separately the development of each science; one has to study the development of all the sciences simultaneously. Besides, it is impossible to separate them satisfactorily one from the other; they grow together and mingle continually in innumerable ways.

While numberless books, many of them excellent, are published every year on the history of literature, of art, of religions, how is it that there is not yet a single history of science that can be compared with the best of them? When so many institutions, libraries, lectureships have been dedicated to the history of everything, how is it that the history of science has been so much neglected?

People who have no knowledge of science, or but slight, are afraid of it. They are not inclined to read a book dealing with the history of science, because they think they are not equal to appreciating it. Now this is a mistake: every intelligent man or woman can understand the development of science, at least if it be properly presented and taken from the beginning. More than that, I am convinced that the historical method is the best for conveying scientific facts and ideas to unprepared minds and to make them thoroughly understandable—at least that is so in the case of grown-up people. On the other hand, those who know science —or are supposed to know it because they have made a special study in some narrow field—are often given to viewing history with contempt. They think that the study of history is hopelessly inaccurate and, according to their own definition of science, unscientific. This is another mistake, which, however, it would take too long to refute completely. Suffice it to say that historical studies, like all other studies, are approximate; the approximation obtained by historians may be looser, but the studies are none the less scientific for that. It is not so much its degree of approximation, as a definite knowledge of this degree, that gives to a study its scientific character.

Scientists and philosophers are at the present time unanimous in wishing that the general tendencies and fundamental principles of science be constantly extricated, criticized and stated with more precision. They are well aware that this is now an essential condition of progress and security. But how will it be possible to conciliate the imperious needs of synthesis and the division of labor?

It would seem that the only possible solution is that which was recommended by Auguste Comte and partly realized by himself and his disciples: namely, to originate a new great specialty, the study of scientific generalities. To secure the unity of knowledge, it will be more and more necessary that some men make a deep study of the principles and of the historical and logical development of all the sciences. Of course, they will not be expected to be perfectly acquainted with all the technical details, but they must have at their command a thorough knowledge of the great lines and of the cardinal facts of each science. It is a very difficult but not an impossible task. The inconveniences of excessive specialization will be happily counterpoised by this new branch of knowledge, which induces a collaboration of philosopher, historian and scientist. It will appear clearly from the following pages that the best instrument of synthesis, and the most natural hyphen between scientist and philosopher is the history of science.

Auguste Comte must be considered as the founder of the history of science, or at least as the first who had a clear and precise, if not a complete, apprehension of it. In his *Cours de philosophie positive*, published from 1830 to 1842, he very clearly brought forward the three fundamental ideas which follow: (1) A synthetic work like his cannot be accomplished without having constant recourse to the history of science; (2) It is necessary to study the evolution of the different sciences to understand the development of the human mind and the history of mankind; (3) It is insufficient to study the history of one or of many particular sciences; one must study the history of all sciences, taken together. Besides this, as early as 1832, Auguste Comte made an application to the minister Guizot for the creation of a chair, devoted to the general history of the sciences (*histoire générale des sciences*). It was sixty years before this wish of his was granted; and the course entrusted to Pierre Laffitte was inaugurated at the Collège de France in 1892, thirty-five years after Comte's death. Another French philosopher, Antoine Cournot, also helped to clear up our ideas by the publication in 1861 of his book *Traité de l'enchaînement des idées fondamentales dans les sciences et dans l'histoire.* However, the real heir to Comte's thought, from our special point of view, is neither Laffitte nor Cournot, but Paul Tannery. It is hardly necessary to say much of him, because all who have the slightest knowledge of the history of science must needs have come across one of his numerous memoirs, all so remarkable for their originality and exactitude. Paul Tannery himself attached importance to his intellectual connection with Comte and often expressed his admiration for the founder of positivism.

Tannery's philosophy is very different from Comte's, but the greatest difference between them is that Comte's knowledge of the history of science was very superficial, whereas Paul Tannery, being extremely learned and having at his disposal a mass of historical research work which did not exist in the thirties, knew more of the history of science than anybody else in the world. Certainly no man ever was better prepared to write a complete history of science, at least of European science, than Paul Tannery. It was his dream to carry out this great work, but unfortunately he died, before realizing his ambition, in 1904.

One can understand the history of science in different ways, but these different conceptions do not contradict each other; they are simply more or less comprehensive. My own conception does not differ much from Tannery's, except that I attach more importance to the psycho-sociological point of view.

Auguste Comte had noticed all the bonds that unite the different sciences, but he did not give enough attention to them. If he had understood that these interactions and this interdependence have existed in all directions from the very beginnings of science, would not the rigid framework of his *Cours de philosophie* have burst asunder?

On the other hand, some people seem to think that it is impossible to write the history of science as a whole, that the subject is too great. I should rather say that the impossibility is to pick out from this inextricable network the development of one single branch of human knowledge. Moreover, it is actually impossible to write the history of any important discovery without writing, willingly or not, a chapter of the history of science—I mean the history of science as a whole. How could we explain, for instance, the discovery of the circulation of the blood if we did not explain the evolution of anatomy, of comparative zoology, of general biology, of natural philosophy, of chemistry, of mechanics? Likewise, to make clear how the determination of longitudes at sea was discovered, little by little, we have to resort to the history of pure and applied mathematics, the history of astronomy and navigation, the history of watch-making, etc. It would be easy enough to give more examples of the same kind.

Further, it is only by considering the history of science as a whole that one can appraise the scientific level of a definite period or of a definite country. It has happened more than once that one science became neglected while others were thriving, or that scientific culture moved from one country to another. But the historian is not deluded by these facts, and he does not think that human genius is suddenly quenched or rekindled; from his synthetical standpoint he sees the torch of light pass from one science to the other or from one people to another. He perceives better than anybody else the continuity of science in space and time, and he is better able to estimate the progress of mankind.

But the historian's mind is not satisfied with the study of the interactions between the different sciences. He wishes to study also the interactions between the different sciences, on one hand, and all the other intellectual or economic phenomena, on the other. As a matter of fact, he has to give a great deal of attention to these reciprocal influences, but of course he does not forget that the aim of his work is essentially to establish the connecting links between scientific ideas.

In short, the purpose of the history of science, as I understand it, is to establish the genesis and the development of scientific facts and ideas, taking into account all intellectual exchanges and all influences brought into play by the very progress of civilization. It is indeed a history of human civilization, considered from its highest point of view. The center of interest is the evolution of science, but general history remains always in the background.

It follows from this definition that the only rational way to subdivide this history is not at all to cut it up according to countries or to sciences, but only according to time. For each period of time, we have to consider at once the whole of its scientific and intellectual development.

Of course, to make this general synthesis possible, it will often be expedient, even necessary, to write monographs or partial syntheses of different kinds. For instance, the study of the archives of a definite place leads naturally to the drawing up of an essay on the history of science in that place. On the other hand, a specialized scientist will be tempted to look up the genealogy of an idea in which he is particularly interested, or to write the biography of a forerunner whose work and genius he can better appreciate than anyone else. But all this research is necessarily incomplete and does not acquire its proper significance so long as it cannot be inserted properly into a history of the sciences of the same age. It may be worth while to add that all monographs are not equally useful; some are so clumsy and absurd that they obscure, mislead and delay the next synthesis.

To elaborate our historical work we have, of course, to use the same methods that are used by ordinary historians to appraise and criticize the materials available to them. But the historian of science has to use, independently, some other methods of a more special nature. I cannot explain them here, but it is easy to understand that, for instance, to establish at what date a discovery became a real part of science and enriched human experience, the historical exegesis must be supplemented by a scientific exegesis, based on the evidence given by the positive sciences.

We must try to marshall all scientific facts and ideas in a definite order; this means that we must try to assign to each of them a date as precise as possible—not the date of their birth or of their publication, but that of their actual incorporation into our knowledge. Likewise, biographers have to exert themselves to find precisely during which periods the influence of great scientists was the most felt, in order to range them in chronological series. This is generally a very difficult thing to do, and the reader will not fail to appreciate the work that is discreetly accomplished by such scholars. Such work of erudition is the bed-rock on which all historical writing is built up.

These remarks complete and add precision to our definition of the history of science. However, it may be well to give some more details about the different exchanges which the historian has to consider in order to put the evolution of science in its proper light.

I shall successively examine some of the other departments of life which are the most interesting for the historian of science: (1) General history or the history of civilization; (2) The history of technology; (3) The history of religions; and (4) The history of fine arts, and arts and crafts.

1. *Science and Civilization.* Since the eighteenth century, and notably under the influence of Vico, Montesquieu and Voltaire, the conception of history has become more and more synthetic. History, the principal interest of which once consisted in military records and court annals, is growing up into a history of civilization. It stands to reason that a sufficient knowledge of the history

of civilization is absolutely necessary for the historian of science, were it only to locate the scientific facts in the very surroundings that gave rise to them.

On the other hand, the historian of civilization can no longer remain unacquainted with the history of science. Some of the most recent historical manuals contain paragraphs devoted to it. It is true, the space allowed is rather scanty, but that is a beginning. I feel confident that, before long, general histories will be written in which the history of science, far from being banished to some obscure corner, will be the very center of the picture. Is not science the most powerful factor of evolution?

Some examples will illustrate the significance of the history of civilization. How can one account for the fact that the Latin manuscripts containing translations of Greek authors made from Arabic texts for so long barred the way to the printed translations that had been elaborated directly from the Greek texts? The latter, indeed, were much better. Björnbo has given some reasons that are very probably the true ones. The printed books that nobody cared to copy became rarer and rarer. On the other hand, the manuscripts were copied over and over again and continually multiplied. Besides, the copyists lacked knowledge and critical sense to a great extent, and they could not help being favorably impressed by the bulk of Arabic literature.

Mere scientific reasons do not suffice to explain the creation of the metric system by the French revolutionaries. This creation was also in part a reaction against the "foot of the king" of the *ancien régime*.

Financial or tariff regulations or the promulgation of labor laws can transform the business life of a country and, indirectly, its scientific production.

To understand the beginnings and development of geography one has to take into account many facts that are quite foreign to science. For instance: the quest for mythical treasures; conquerors' ambitions; religious proselytism; the adventurous instincts of daring young men.

Lastly, it is necessary to know the history of epidemics and to study all the social facts that have been their causes or their results, to estimate correctly the evolution of medical ideas.

2. *Science and Technology*. Industrial requirements are always putting new questions to science, and in this way they guide, so to say, its evolution. On the other hand, the progress of science continually gives birth to new industries or brings new life to old ones. It follows that the history of science is constantly interwoven with the history of technology, and that it is impossible to separate one from the other.

Let us see some examples. After exhaustion-pumps had been invented, there was such a demand for good pumps of this kind that special workshops were founded in the beginning of the eighteenth century, in Leyden, Holland, to make them, and of course these workshops soon undertook to make other scientific instruments. It is hardly necessary to point out how intimately connected the making of these instruments is with the history of physics or astronomy.

A geological discovery suffices to revolutionize a whole country and transform an agricultural nation into an industrial one. Of course, a transformation as complete as this involves a radical change in scientific needs. The working of mines has always exerted such a deep influence on the evolution of science and civilization that one might compare the importance of mines in the history of science with that of temples in the history of art. L. de Launay has very clearly shown that the silver mines in Laurion played a considerable part in the history of Greece.

The history of chemistry would sometimes be unintelligible if the history of chemical industries was not studied at the same time. Let me simply remind the reader of the case of coloring matters. Industrial research made in this direction has deeply influenced the progress of organic chemistry. On the other hand, it is well known how much has been done to improve this industry by the scientists of the German Chemical Society.

A chemical discovery can revolutionize a whole country, just as completely as a geological one; as soon as it becomes possible to realize, on a business basis, the chemical synthesis of a natural product (like indigo, vanilla, India rubber), the agricultural industry and civilization of immense countries are in danger.

Technical inventions are more precisely determined every day by industrial needs. The manufacturer can often say very definitely to the inventor: "This is the invention which I now need to improve my production." Besides, every invention starts a series of others that the first has made necessary and that it would have been impossible to realize, or even to conceive, previously.

Lastly, commercial needs also influence the development of the sciences, not only the natural sciences and geography (that is too obvious to dwell upon), but even mathematics. It is necessary to take into account the evolution of book-keeping and banking business to understand thoroughly the introduction and the spread of Hindu-Arabic numerals into Europe, and later the invention of decimal fractions. It is also owing in great measure to commercial requirements that many astronomical discoveries were made, and that the different systems of weights and measures were created.

3. *Science and Religion.* Science and religion have never ceased to influence one another, even in our own time and in the countries where science has reached a high degree of perfection and independence. But of course the younger science was, and the farther we go back through the ages, the more numerous these interactions are. Primitive people cannot separate scientific or technical ideas from religious ones, or, more exactly, this classification has no sense to them. Later, when the division of labor had created some scientists or engineers, distinct from the priests, or at least had given birth to a class of priests who had undergone a higher scientific training than their colleagues, even then the interpretation of the holy books, the observance of rites, the needs of agriculture and medicine, the making of the calendar, and above all, the hopes, the fears and the anxieties of a very precarious exist-

ence, have been innumerable links between science and religion. The great plagues, and generally all cataclysms, for instance earthquakes or wars, have been followed by religious revivals and often by violent outbursts of religious fanaticism.

On the other hand I know many cases where the priests themselves have been the transmitters of knowledge from one generation to the following. The best example of this can be found during the period extending from the end of the second school of Alexandria to the ninth century. We owe, if not the advancement of science, at least its conservation, to the doctors of the Latin and Greek churches, to the Nestorians and other heretics.

In some other cases the influence of religion is less direct, but not less important. For instance, A. de Candolle has proved that the Protestant families which were exiled from the Catholic countries of Europe during the sixteenth and seventeenth centuries and even during the eighteenth, have given birth to an extraordinarily high number of distinguished scientists. This is not to be wondered at. These people who preferred the misery of exile to moral servitude were certainly above the average in their conscientiousness and earnestness.

The interactions between science and religion have often had an aggressive character. There has been, most of the time, a real warfare. But, as a matter of fact, it is not a warfare between science and *religion*—there can be no warfare between them—but between science and *theology*. It is true that the man in the street does not easily differentiate between religious feelings and faith, on one side, and dogmas, rites and religious formalism, on the other. It is true also that the theologians, while affecting that religion itself was aimed at when they alone were criticized, have not ceased from aggravating these misunderstandings. An excellent proof of this has been given in this country. One of the great men of these United States, Andrew Dickson White, published a splendid book on *The Warfare Between Science and Theology*. Mr. White was a very godly man, and his book is, it is hardly necessary to state, extremely liberal and indulgent to everybody. Notwithstanding this, the author and his book had to bear the attacks of a great many fanatics.

One of the saddest results of these misunderstandings is that some very religious and sincere souls have been misled and have treated science as an enemy. Another important result is that the evolution of science is very intimately interwoven with that of religions and their heresies.

4. *Science and Art*. It may be useful to tender some remarks upon the different characteristics of scientific and artistic work before pointing out what is interesting from our point of view in the history of art. In the history of art as it is generally taught, very little is said about technicalities. Are there many people who know, or care to know, what kind of colors Botticelli used, or what were the tools of Phidias? We love a work of art for itself. It is essentially the ultimate result that interests us, not the methods used to obtain it. In the domain of learning, on the contrary, the result is generally less interesting than the methods employed to reach it.

The history of science is not merely a history of the conquests of the human mind, but it is much more a study of the instruments—material and intellectual instruments—created by our intelligence; it is also a history of human experience. This long experience of the past has much more significance for the scientist than for the artist. The artist admires the work of his forerunners, but the scientist does more than admire, he makes actual use of it. The artist may find an inspiration in it, but the scientist tries to incorporate it entirely in his own work. It is very difficult to conceive progress in art. Does Rodin carve better than Verrocchio or Polycletus? The pictures by Carrière, by Watts, or by Segantini: are they finer than those by Fra Angelico, by Van Eyck or by Moro? Have these questions even any sense?

In the domain of science the matter is quite different. Undoubtedly it would be foolish to discuss whether Archimedes was more or less intelligent than Newton or Gauss; but we can in all security assert that Gauss knew more than Newton, and that Newton knew more than Archimedes. The making of knowledge, unlike that of beauty, is essentially a cumulative process. By the way, this is the reason why the history of science should be the leading thread in the history of civilization. Nothing that has been done or invented gets lost. Every contribution, great or small, is appreciated and classified. This cumulative process is so obvious that even very young men may be better informed and more learned than their most illustrious forerunners. As a matter of fact, they are standing on the shoulders of their predecessors, and so they have a chance to see further. If they are not very intelligent they may be inclined to think that it is useless to study history, under the misapprehension that they already know from the past all that is really worth knowing. In short, we are not sure that men become more intelligent—that is, whether intelligence increases—but we know positively that human experience and knowledge grow every day. As I have said, one does not pay much heed to mediocre artists. What they do has not much importance. On the contrary, in the laboratories, libraries and museums where science is slowly growing—like an ever-living tree—enormous quantities of excellent work is done by thousands of men who are not unusually intelligent, but who have been well trained, have good methods and plenty of patience.

Scientific work is the result of an international collaboration, the organization of which is perfected every day. Thousands of scientists devote their whole lives to this collective work—like bees in a hive—but their hive is the world. This collaboration does not take place simply in space, but also in time; the oldest astronomical observations are still of some use. Perhaps this collective nature of scientific work is one of the causes of the general indifference concerning its history—indifference strongly contrasting with the widespread curiosity about the history of literature and the fine arts. Science aims at objectivity; the scientist exerts himself to decrease to a minimum his "personal equation." Works of art, on the contrary, are extremely individual and passionate; so it is not to be wondered at that they excite more sympathy and interest.

The history of the fine arts and of literature is generally considered as a history of the great artists and of the works they have bequeathed to us. But one could adopt a different point of view: just as the history of science gives us the materials of an evolution of human intellect, so one could look to the history of arts and of literature for the story of the evolution of human sensibility. The history of science is a history of ideas; just so the history of art could be considered as a history of man's dreams. Understood in this way, the two histories complete and enlighten one another.

The interactions between science and art have been particularly vivid at times in naturalistic reactions against scholastic and pedantic excesses. It would be extremely interesting to make a closer study of the rhythm of the different tendencies that swayed plastic arts and music, and to look for similar rhythms in the contemporary succession of scientific theories, or more exactly, attitudes. The appearance of men of genius, who were at one and the same time artists and scientists—such as Leonardo da Vinci, Albrecht Dürer and Bernard Palissy—gives us a splendid opportunity to study these interactions in their deepest and most fascinating form. On the other hand, it is a fact that scientific ideas have often been transmitted by works of art; moreover, for all the period preceding the beginnings of popular printing, these works of art give us direct testimonies—often the only ones we have—of inestimable value. For instance, it would be impossible to trace the history of ancient chemistry but for all the works of art and decoration that have come to us; and, to understand the history of chemistry, not only in ancient times but even up to the threshold of the seventeenth century, it is still necessary to study the development of the arts and crafts—the art of the potter, glassmaker, chaser, jeweler, miniature-painter, and enameler.

But the history of art helps us, above all, to understand the spirit and the soul of vanished civilizations. From this point of view, works of art have an immense superiority over every other manifestation of the human mind; they give us a complete and synthetical view of times gone by; they offer us the information that we need at a glance; they bring the past to life again. A granite sphinx, a Nike, a picture by Giotto or by Breughel, a Gothic cathedral, a mass by Palestrina—all these things teach us more in one flash than living men could do by long discourses.

The following examples will show what kind of information the history of art can give us. It is by comparing various monuments that Viollet le Duc has been able to find out some of the principal commercial roads of the twelfth century. Illustrations from Roman monuments give us exact information as to the origin of domestic and medical plants. Indeed, it is through Greece and Rome that most of them were introduced from the East into Europe. The history of these plants tells us all the vicissitudes that modified the commercial and intellectual relations between those peoples. Here is another very curious fact. The great botanist H. de Vries discovered the variety *monophylla* of *Fragaria vesca* in a picture by Holbein the Elder ("The Saint Sebastian of Munich," dated 1516). This variety is now cultivated in botanic gardens as a rarity. One guesses that similar discoveries, however small they may appear, sometimes accomplish the solution of historical problems.

Lastly, I wish to note that the history of science is also, to a certain extent—perhaps less than some mathematicians think, but much more than the artists suppose—a history of taste. Leaving aside the external beauty of many books of science, for many scientists were splendid writers (think of Galileo, Descartes, Pascal, Goethe, Darwin), the very substance of their work has often a great aesthetic value. Scientists who are men of taste very easily distinguish the scientific theories that are beautiful and elegant from the others. It would be wrong to ignore this distinction, because this beauty and harmony, that the average person cannot see but that the scientist does see, is extremely deep and significant. One might ask: "These theories that are more beautiful—are they more true?" Anyhow, they are easier to grasp and more fertile; and for these reasons alone it is worth while to give them our preference.

THE SCIENTIFIC POINT OF VIEW

The history of science has a great heuristic value, especially if it has been worked out by somebody who is as well acquainted with modern scientific tendencies as with ancient ones. The sequence of old discoveries suggests similar concatenations to the scientist, and so enables him to make new discoveries. Disused methods, cleverly modified, may be rendered efficient again. When this is understood, the history of science becomes really a research method. A great scientist of our own time, Ostwald, has even gone so far as to say that, "It is nothing but a research method." We do not admit that much. Anyhow, new and old science complete and continuously help one another to advance and to diminish the unknown that surrounds us everywhere. Does this idea not illuminate our conception of universal scientific collaboration? Death itself does not interrupt the scientist's work. Theories once unfolded are eternally living and acting.

To give to our history all its heuristic value, it is not sufficient to retrace the progress of the human mind. It is also necessary to remember the regressions, the sudden halts, the mishaps of all kinds that have interrupted its course. The history of errors is extremely useful; for one thing, because it helps us to better appreciate the evolution of truth; also because it enables us to avoid the same mistakes in the future; lastly, because the errors of science are of a relative nature. The truths of today will perhaps be considered tomorrow, if not as complete mistakes, at least as very incomplete truths; and who knows whether the errors of yesterday will not be the approximate truths of tomorrow? Similar rehabilitations frequently occur, and the results of historical research often oblige us to admire and honor people who have been misunderstood and despised in their own time. This incidentally proves that the study of the history of science has also some moral advantages.

However, the history of superstitions and errors must not make us forget that it is the history of truth—the most complete and the highest truths—that interests us primarily. Besides, one may aim at retracing the history of truth in its entirety, because it is naturally limited; but the history of errors is infinite! Therefore it is necessary to fix some artificial limits to the latter and to choose judiciously between the errors and the superstitions. A great simplification is obtained by classifying the errors in groups. Indeed, the same mistakes and superstitions appear over and over again in different shapes, and it is useful to know the various types of errors in order to understand the mechanism of intellect.

It is much to be regretted that many scientists decline to admit the utility of historical research, or consider it simply as a kind of pastime of small importance. They base their contempt on the following argument: "All the best of ancient science has been assimilated and incorporated in our own science. The rest only deserves oblivion, and it is awkward to over-burden our memory with it. The science that we are learning and teaching is the result of a continuous selection which has eliminated all the parasitic parts in order to retain only that which is of real value."

It is easy to see that this argument is not sound. For one thing, who will guarantee that the successive selections have been well made? This is so much the more a matter of doubt in that this selective and synthetic work is generally done not by men of genius, but by professors, by authors of textbooks, vulgarizers of all kinds, whose judgment is not necessarily irreproachable and whose intuitions are not always successful. Besides, as science is constantly evolving, and as new points of view are introduced every day, any idea that has been neglected may be considered later on as very important and fertile. It often happens also that some facts, scarcely known, all at once become very interesting, because they can be inserted into a new theory that they help to illustrate. Of course scientific syntheses—such as those represented by our textbooks—are indispensable. Without them science could hardly be transmitted from one generation of students to the next, but it must be understood that they are always provisional and precarious. They must be periodically revised. Now, how would that be possible if the history of science did not show us our way through all the unutilized experience of the past? History is, so to say, the guide, the catalogue without which new syntheses and selections made from fresh points of view would hardly be possible. All the vicissitudes and recantations of science prove conclusively that no man can ever flatter himself that he has definitely and completely exhausted a scientific fact or theory. No particle of human experience, however small, can be entirely neglected. To assert this is to assert, at the same time, the necessity of historical research.

Moreover, among scientific works there are some, the genesis of which cannot be explained in the ordinary analytical way. They introduce abrupt discontinuities into the evolution of science, because they so far anticipate their own time. These works of genius are never entirely explored, and the interest they offer is never entirely exhausted. It is perhaps because it is almost inexhaustible, that true genius is so mysterious. Sometimes centuries pass before the doctrines of a man of genius are appraised at their true value. A great deal of benefit is still to be reaped from reading in the works of Aristotle, Diophantus, Huygens or Newton. They are full of hidden treasures. It is a gross mistake to think that there is nothing more in such works than the facts and ideas which are positively formulated; if that were true, of course, it would be useless to refer to them: the enunciation of these facts and ideas would suffice. But that is not true, and I cannot but advise those who have any doubt about it, to try. They will find that nothing excites the mind more than this return to the sources. Here, also, it is the historian's business to point out to the scientist the very sources where he will most likely invigorate his mind and start a fresh impulse.

I wish now to give a few examples to illustrate the preceding remarks. Any amount of them can be found in the history of medicine; we need but recall how greatly the whole of medical evolution has been influenced by the Hippocratic teaching, our modern ideas on humorism and naturism; or, again, the organo-therapeutic theories. Not only are the old ideas restored to vogue, but it sometimes seems that a kind of rhythm brings them back to light periodically. Georges Bohn has shown the periodical return, in the domain of comparative psychology, on one hand, of the animistic and anthropomorphic conceptions, and on the other hand, of the positivist conceptions. As a rule, the further science is removed from the mathematical form, the more likely these vicissitudes are. One can also say that when science is more accurate, that is to say, when the domain of uncertainty and hypothesis becomes narrower, the oscillations of the mind between divergent points of view are so much the less numerous,—but they do not cease entirely. Thus E. Belot reintroduced into cosmology, in a very seductive shape, the vortex theory that one would have thought had been entirely banished by Newton's criticisms. Similarly weighty reasons exist for reinstating into optics the emission theory, which seemed to have been forever exploded by the discoveries of Huygens, Young and Fresnel.

But the best examples of such return to ancient knowledge are given to us by the history of technology. The history of chemical industries is very significant from this point of view: this is due to the fact that here economic conditions play a considerable part. In order that an invention may be realized it does not suffice that it be theoretically possible; it must pay. Now thousands of circumstances continually modify the material factors which the engineer is struggling with; many are of such a nature that nobody could foresee them, or (what amounts to the same thing), that it would cost too much to insure oneself against all of them. If new products appear on the market, or if the prices of some of the raw materials happen to vary considerably, or if new discoveries are made, or if new residues are to be employed, old methods that were once too expensive may become economical, or vice versa. Hence the chemist and the engineer have a vital interest in knowing the processes that have fallen into disuse, but to which the very progress of science may give from one day to the next a new career. The history of science is to them, so to say, what abandoned mines are to the prospector.

But in my opinion, however important its heuristic value may be, there are still deeper reasons why the scientist should give his attention to the history of science. I am thinking of those which have been so splendidly illustrated by Ernst Mach in his *Mechanics*. For one thing, it is obvious that "they that know the entire course of the development of science will, as a matter of course, judge more freely and more correctly of the significance of any present scientific movement than they who, limited in their views to the age in which their own lives have been spent, contemplate merely the momentary trend that the course of intellectual events takes at the present moment." In other words, in order to understand and appraise at its just value what one possesses, it is well to know what the people possessed who came before us; this is as true in the domain of science as it is in daily life. It is historical knowledge that discloses to the scientist his precise attitude toward the problems with which he has to grapple, and that enables him to dominate them.

Moreover, while research workers exert themselves to extend the boundaries of science, other scientists are more anxious to ascertain whether the scaffolding is really solid, and whether their more and more daring and complex edifices do not risk giving way. Now the task of the latter, which is neither less important nor less lofty than that of discovery, necessarily implies a return to the past. *This critical work is essentially of an historical nature.* While it helps to make the whole fabric of science more coherent and more rigorous, at the same time it brings to light all the accidental and conventional parts of it, and so it opens new horizons to the discoverer's mind. If that work were not done, science would soon degenerate into a system of prejudices; its principles would become metaphysical axioms, dogmas, a new kind of revelation.

That is what some scientists come to, who, for fear of falling into literature or "metaphysics" (as they put it), banish all historical or philosophic considerations. Alas! the exclusive worship of positive facts makes them sink into the worst kind of metaphysics —scientific idolatry.

Fortunately, it happens at certain periods of evolution that resounding and paradoxical discoveries make an inventory and a thorough survey of our knowledge more obviously necessary to everybody. We are fortunate enough to be living at one of these critical and most interesting periods.

The purpose of historical criticism is not merely to render science more accurate, but also to bring order and clarity into it, to simplify it. Indeed, it is the survey of the past that enables us best to extricate what is really essential. The importance of a concept appears in a much better light when one has taken the trouble to consider all the difficulties that were surmounted to reach it, all the errors with which it was entangled, in short, all the previous life that has given birth to it. One could say that the riches and fertility of a concept are a function of its heredity, and that alone makes it worth while to study its genealogy.

The history of science is accomplishing an endless purification of scientific facts and ideas. It enables us to deepen them, which is undoubtedly the best way to make them simpler. This simplification is, of course, the more necessary as science grows bigger and more intricate. By the way, it is thanks to this progressive simplification that an encyclopedic knowledge does not become utterly impossible; in certain cases it becomes even more accessible. For instance, is it not easier to study chemistry or astronomy—I mean the essentials of it—now than it was, say, in the fifteenth century?

I think one can infer from all the preceding remarks that no scientist is entitled to claim a profound and complete knowledge of his branch of science if he is not acquainted with its history. I have compared the scientific achievements of mankind with the collective work that the bees accomplish in their hives. This comparison is particularly apposite to the scientists who have specialized to excess and work diligently in their own narrow field, ignoring the rest of the world. Such men are doubtless necessary, as are the bees that provide honey. But their endeavors could never give birth to a systematic knowledge, to a science proper. It is the more necessary that other scientists raise themselves above the artificial partitions of the different specialties. Their investigations irresistibly lead them to the study of history, and they obtain from it a deeper apprehension of their own collaboration in the grand undertakings of mankind. Just as one experiences gratification in knowing where one is and why, similarly it gives them pleasure to locate their own task in the world's work and to grasp better its relative import. And also, they understand, better than others do, the significance of the thousand and one ties that connect them to their fellowmen—and the power of human solidarity, without which there would be no science.

THE PEDAGOGIC POINT OF VIEW

Science is generally taught in a much too synthetical way.* It may be that this method is indeed the best for the average student who passively accepts the master's authority. But those whose philosophical mind is more awake can hardly be satisfied by this food, the preparation of which is unknown to them. Instead of being assuaged by harmonious order and perfect science, they are devoured by doubt and anxiety: "Why does the master teach us so? Why has he chosen those definitions? Why?" Not that they are loath to use synthetical methods; on the contrary, these young men will probably be the first to admire the depth and elegance of such teaching once they have grasped from their own experience its logical appositeness, its generality and its

---

* My experience refers especially to the European continent and to the teaching of the physical and mathematical sciences.

economy. But first of all they want to know "how all that was built up," and their minds instinctively recoil from a dogmatism that is still arbitrary to them.

It remains arbitrary indeed so long as the reasons that justify and render natural one arrangement in preference to any other have not been explained. I know that it is not easy to teach beginners in this way, but at least the deficiences of the present methods could be tempered, and I do not ask for more.

Nothing would be more useful from this point of view than to work out some textbooks in which science would be expounded in chronological order; this is indeed a very important task for which Ernst Mach has given us some admirable models. These textbooks would not be employed for elementary study, unless the pupils used them at the same time as others composed along dogmatic lines. Students should be asked to study the latter and read the former. But in my opinion, these historical textbooks would especially stand professors in good stead, by enabling them to illustrate their lessons and make them more intuitive. Oral teaching, more pliable than written teaching, would easily admit of short historical digressions. Would not the students more easily remember the abstract truths that are impressed upon them in ever-increasing quantities, if their memory could lay hold of some live facts?

But that does not exhaust the pedagogic importance of the history of science. Nothing is better fitted to awaken a pupil's critical sense and to test his vocation than to retrace for him in detail the complete history of a discovery, to show him the trammels of all kinds that constantly arise in the inventor's path, to show him also how one surmounts them or evades them, and lastly how one draws closer and closer to the goal without ever reaching it. Besides, this historical initiation would cure the young students of the unfortunate habit of thinking that science began with *them*.

Good scientific biographies also have a great educational value; they lead an adolescent's imagination in the best direction. Critical and sincere biographies make excellent contributions to the history of mankind. Would not the students work with a better heart and more enthusiasm, would they not have a deeper respect for science, if they knew a little more about the heroes who have built it up, stone by stone, at the expense of so much suffering, struggle and perseverance? Would they not be more eager to undertake some disinterested research work? Or, at least, would they not better appreciate the greatness and beauty of the whole if they had, more or less, partaken of the joy and intoxication of seeing it accomplished amidst continuous difficulties?

Lastly, the history of science—even more than ordinary history —is a general education in itself. It familiarizes us with the ideas of evolution and continuous transformation of human things; it makes us understand the relative and precarious nature of all our knowledge; it sharpens our judgment; it shows us that, if the accomplishments of mankind as a whole are really grand, the contribution of each of us is, in the main, small, and that even the greatest amongst us ought to be modest. It helps to make scientists who are not mere scientists, but also men and citizens.

THE PSYCHOLOGICAL AND SOCIOLOGICAL POINTS OF VIEW

The history of science, its birth, its evolution, its diffusion, its progress and regressions, irresistibly imposes upon us a series of psychological problems. We here enter the field of "universal history," such as the much-lamented Karl Lamprecht has defined it; for the history of science in the main amounts to psychosociological investigation.

It is necessary to make a preliminary distinction. The progress of science is due to two different kinds of causes: (1) Purely psychological causes, the intellectual work of the scientist; (2) Material causes, principally the appearance of new subject matter or the use of improved scientific tools. Of course, it is not difficult to show that the origin of these material causes is itself more or less of a psychological nature. But the distinction holds good; a discovery has not the same character, the same psychological importance, if it is the almost automatic result of a technical improvement, as it would have if it were the fruit of a mind's reaction.

We propose to discover the general laws of the intellectual evolution of mankind, if such laws exist. These studies might also help us to better understand the intellect's mechanism. But of course we have given up the extravagant idea of establishing a priori the conditions of scientific development. On the contrary our aim is to deduce them from a thorough analysis of all the accumulated experience of the past.

The best instrument for these studies is the comparative method, and this means that we must not expect to reach a degree of accuracy of which this method does not admit. But no scientific work would be possible in the domain of biology and sociology if we did not have the wisdom and patience to be satisfied with the approximation that is within our reach. The comparisons may be confined to the realm of science; I would call these the "internal" comparisons. They may also be made between the evolution of scientific phenomena and that of other intellectual or economic phenomena; and these I would call the "external" comparisons. The greatest difficulty, of course, is to find evolutionary processes that can be adequately compared and that are sufficiently independent one of another.

The application of this method has already supplied some results which have been very improperly called "historical laws," and the exactitude of which is very variable. The following are some examples which I list but shall refrain from discussing. Paul Tannery has shown that the development of calculation generally precedes that of geometry. In their choice of decorative elements, primitive peoples always pass from animals to plants; they never do the contrary. The hypothesis that has been expressed about the course of civilization from the South and the East to the North and West, is well known. Remember also the law of historical periods proposed by Lamprecht, and especially the famous law of the three states (*la loi des trois états*), formulated by Auguste Comte. The theory of historical materialism, originated by Karl Marx, is also a proper example.

It is sensible to undertake the study of intellectual activities in the same way that we study the industry of the beavers or the bees. Of the work produced by the human brain we generally know nothing but the results, but these are tangible and can be, if not actually measured, at least compared and appraised with more or less precision. The invention of a machine or the discovery of a natural law: are these not, at bottom, phenomena of the same kind as the behavior of a crab or of a sea anemone under determined circumstances? They are, of course, much more complex and their study requires the use of new methods, scarcely explored; but can one not admit, at least as a working hypothesis, that they do not differ in essentials? The psychology of the superior functions of the brain is not necessarily more complicated than that of the inferior functions; I should be rather inclined to think the contrary. For instance, would it not be easier to retrace the development of a scientific idea in a clear mind than to disentangle, in the "pre-logical" head of a primitive man, the obscure roots of his instinct of property or imitation?

It is from the comparison of these intellectual facts, as they can be collected by the historian of science from the whole intellectual experience of the world, that we may try to deduce the laws of thought. Human experience has been continuously increasing during the ages, but the intellect itself—has it evolved? The methods of discovery, the mental experiences, the hidden mechanism of intuition—have they not remained somewhat the same?

Is there nothing invariable in men's intellectual behavior? What are those invariants, or at least those relative invariants, those more stable parts of ourselves? To what extent does the scientific environment exert its influence upon the scientists, and *vice versa*? How do social activities evidence themselves in the domain of science? By what mental processes are the ideas of the initiators integrated in the collective thought, to become, by and by, common notions? All these questions, raised by the history of science, are so many psychological problems.

As to research concerning the psychology of invention, choice materials will be found in the history of technology. The results of technical invention are material objects of a very concrete and tangible nature. Besides, the mechanism of industrial discoveries is especially interesting, because to materialize his ideas the engineer has actually to struggle with all the difficulties of real life. The struggle is more obvious here than in any other domain. It frequently happens that unexpected obstacles are so great that the idea cannot be carried out; but it also happens very often that the very clash of these obstacles gives birth to new ideas, deeper and richer than the original ones. Then one sees, so to say, the invention gush out from the conflict between matter and spirit.

It would be apposite here to present some remarks about the "genealogical" research work that was initiated by Francis Galton and Alphonse de Candolle. These very interesting historico-statistical investigations, intimately connected with the eugenic movement, bring new testimonies to the importance of the history of science from the psycho-sociological point of view. But, in order to give a good idea of these studies, I should be obliged to make too long a digression from my subject.

THE HUMANISTIC POINT OF VIEW

A deeper knowledge and a greater diffusion of the history of science will help to bring about a new "humanism." (I beg the reader to excuse me for using a word that has already been employed in at least two different senses, but I do not find any other that is more adequate to the idea I wish to convey.) The history of science, if it is understood in a really philosophic way, will broaden our horizon and sympathy; it will raise our intellectual and moral standards; it will deepen our comprehension of men and nature. The humanistic movement of the Renaissance was essentially a synthetic movement. The humanists were longing

for a new atmosphere and a broader conception of life; their
curiosity was insatiable. We have at least this much in common
with them. We know also that if science were to be abandoned to
narrow-minded specialists, it would soon degenerate into a new
kind of scholasticism, without life or beauty—false and wrong like
death itself. This would be another good reason for comparing
our task with that accomplished by the former humanists. However, their movement was essentially toward the past; ours is
much more a movement toward the future.

Science, divided into water-tight compartments, makes us feel
uneasy;—a world split into selfish and quarrelsome nations (similar to the Italian and Flemish municipalities of the Renaissance)
is too narrow for us. We need the full experience of other countries, of other races; we need also the full experience of other ages.
We need more air!

It may be useful to lay some stress on the significance of science
from the international point of view. Science is the most precious
patrimony of mankind. It is immortal. It is inalienable. It cannot
but increase. Does not this precious patrimony deserve to be
known thoroughly, not only in its present state but in its whole
evolution? Now most men—most scientists—are unfamiliar with
the glorious history of our conquests over nature. Would it not be
a great work of peace and progress to bring them to better understanding and appreciation of this intellectual domain which is
privileged among all others, *because it is the only one that is
entirely common to all?* Science is not only the strongest tie, but
it is the only one that is really strong and undisputed.

Science makes for peace more than anything else in the world;
it is the cement that holds together the highest and the most comprehensive minds of all countries, of all races, of all creeds. Every
nation derives benefit from the discoveries that have been made
by the others.

Just as scientific methods are the basis of well-nigh all our
knowledge, just so science appears more and more as the bedrock
on which every organization has to be built up to be strong and

fertile. It is the most powerful factor of human progress. As Mach has perfectly put it: "Science has undertaken to replace wavering and unconscious adaptation by a methodical adaptation, quicker and decidedly conscious." It is the historian's duty to evidence all the scientific facts and ideas that make for peace and civilization; in this way he will make science's cultural function more secure.

The international significance of the history of science has not been better grasped thus far, for the simple reason that very few historical studies have been inspired by a real international spirit. For one thing, universal histories have been almost exclusively devoted to the achievements of the Indo-Aryan race. Everything in them gravitates round the development of Europe. Of course this point of view is absolutely false. The history of mankind is too obviously incomplete if it does not include, on the same level as the Western experience, the immense experience of the East. We badly need the knowledge and wisdom of Asia. They have found other solutions to our own problems (the fundamental problems cannot but be the same) and it is of the greatest importance to consider these solutions, and to consider them with humility. They have very often been nearer to truth and beauty than we. Besides, although the development of the Far Eastern countries has been to a great extent independent of our own, there have been far more exchanges, especially in ancient times, than is generally believed, and it is of paramount importance to investigate these matters.

The progress of mankind is not simply an economic development; it is much more an intellectual unfolding, as Henry Thomas Buckle has shown with so much force. The whole course of civilization is marked by the triumph of the mental laws over the physical—a triumph of man over nature. But to my mind, Buckle has even gone too far in this direction. I am not ready to concede his claim that the changes in every civilized people are dependent solely on three things: (1) The amount of knowledge of the ablest men; (2) The direction of this knowledge; (3) Its diffusion.

If Buckle were right all history would be included in the history of science. There are other things to consider.

Moral factors do not deserve the contempt which Buckle showed them and I think that it is even possible to construct an ethical interpretation of history. To give a moral significance to history, the essential condition is to make it as complete, as sincere as possible. Nothing is more demoralizing than histories *ad usum Delphini*. We must display the whole of human experience, the best and worst together. The greatest achievement of mankind is indeed its struggle against evil and ignorance. Nothing is nobler than this endless struggle between the truth of to-day and that of yesterday. It stands to reason that if one side of the picture is not shown—the evil side, for instance—the other loses a great deal of its interest. The quest for truth and beauty is indeed man's glory. This is certainly the highest moral interpretation which history allows.

We must try to humanize science, better to show its various relations with other human activities—its relation to our own nature. It will not lower science; on the contrary, science remains the center of human evolution and its highest goal; to humanize it is not to make it less important, but more significant, more impressive, more amiable.

The new humanism—as I venture to call the intellectual movement that has been defined in the preceding pages—will also have the following consequences: it will disentangle us from many local and national prejudices, also from many of the common prejudices of our own time. Each age has, of course, its own prejudices. Just as the only way to get rid of local prejudices is to travel,—similarly, to extricate ourselves from time-narrowness, we must wander through the ages. Our age is not necessarily the best or the wisest, and anyhow it is not the last! We have to prepare the next one, and I hope a better one.

If we study history, it is not through mere curiosity, simply to know how things happened in the olden times (if we have no other purpose than this, our knowledge would indeed be of a poor quality) ; nor is it for the mere intellectual joy of understanding life better. We are not disinterested enough for that. No; we wish to understand, to foresee more clearly; we wish to be able to act with more precision and wisdom. History itself is of no concern to us. The past does not interest us but for the future.

To build up this future, to make it beautiful, as were those glorious times of synthetic knowledge, for instance that of Phidias or of Leonardo da Vinci, it is necessary to prepare a new synthesis. We propose to realize it by bringing about a new and more intimate collaboration between scientist, philosopher and historian. If that could be accomplished, it would give birth to so much beauty that the collaboration of the artist would also, necessarily, be secured; an age of synthesis is always an age of art. This synthesis is what I call "the new humanism." It is something in the making—not a dream. We see it growing, but no one can tell how big it will grow.

The writer is convinced that the history of science—that is to say, the history of human thought and civilization in its broadest form—is the indispensable basis of any philosophy. *History is but a method—not an aim!*

PART TWO

SECRET HISTORY

4. SECRET HISTORY

The history of mankind is double: political history which is to a large extent a history of the masses, and intellectual history which is largely the history of a few individuals.

The first development is the obvious one; it is the one which has thus far claimed the attention of historians almost exclusively. The peoples of the earth and, within each nation, the different classes of men, are not equally fertile, ingenious, energetic, ambitious. Their ambition—in the case of peoples one calls it, often, imperialism—is a function of their strength and vitality. If they become conscious of their superiority without being restrained by moral or religious motives, they are bound to become aggressive. Between strong, numerous, hungry people on the one hand and a people, weak and few in number, on the other, there arises, so to say, a difference of potential which, if it reaches a certain limit, causes a sudden disruption—war or revolution. Political or economic history can thus be explained in terms of forces chiefly material. (At least in theory, for in most cases the complexity of causes is too great to admit of a strict analysis and we must be content to register most historical disruptions as we register earthquakes or cyclones: we know the causes but only in a general way, and our grasp of them is very weak.) To be sure, other factors than the material must be considered—moral and religious factors, for instance,—but the fundamental causes are material. Leaders may exert a deep influence and modify the course of events, but only to a limited extent, for their energy remains always a function of the energy of their following. They can lead only to the extent to which they avail themselves of existing passions, of the differences of potential which already obtain: they cannot create these differences, but they can make use of them in various ways; they can delay the discharge or else provoke it and modify its nature.

The second development is far less obvious; in fact so far as the

majority of people is concerned, *it is almost secret.* Yet it is the
development of the activities which are most specifically human,
the development of all that is best in humanity: I mean the development of art, of science, of justice, of moral and religious
ideals; in short, the creation and evolution of spiritual values.
These values are created by individuals; in most cases isolated
individuals. Caesar and Napoleon cannot accomplish their destiny
without the collaboration of millions; Spinoza, Newton, Pasteur
do accomplish their own in seclusion. They thrive best in solitude.
The elaboration of their sacred task—the very fulfillment of
human destiny—is to a large degree independent of circumstances.
At least, external circumstances seem purely accidental, not really
creative. Society can poison Socrates, crucify Jesus or behead
Lavoisier; it cannot cause them to be born, it cannot dictate
their task.

It is a very great pleasure to reveal to young students this
second but essential aspect of human history—the course of
human progress—for they know generally but little of it, and
what they know has been obscured by the large mass of irrelevant
and indifferent facts. They see kings enthroned, peoples in arms;
they hear the clash of armies or of mobs; they may even hear the
impassioned orations of statesmen or rebels. But how could they
see the poor philosopher working in his miserable quarters; the
artist wrung under the load of his inspiration; the scientist pursuing silently, obstinately, his self-imposed quest? It requires more
wisdom and imagination than they can possibly have to see these
things. They may know pretty well the historical background. It
is the inestimable privilege of the historian of science to place in
front of it these inconspicuous but central figures.

Who cares to know the great business men and the financiers
of Greece or Rome or of the Renaissance? Their very names are
forgotten. The very few of them who escaped oblivion did so
only because they patronized the disinterested activity of scholars, artists and scientists. Yet in spite of the high regard which

mankind has for those who minister successfully to its material needs, as soon as they are dead and mankind's judgment is no longer influenced by these needs, such men are thrown into the background and their servants—artists and scientists—come into the center of the stage. The sober judgment of mankind thus confirms our assumption: the few men who enrich its spiritual life are its true representatives in the light of eternity. Are we not right then in believing that it is they, and no others, who fulfill its destiny?

This enables us finally to solve another paradox: how can one reconcile the unity of mankind with a chronic state of distrust, of discord and war, alas! all too obvious? Quite simply; the unity is hidden but deep-seated; the disunity widespread but superficial. The unity is felt and expressed primarily by the few men of all nations whose aims are not selfish, or provincial, nationalistic, racial or sectarian in any way, but largely human: the very few men upon whom has devolved the fulfillment of mankind's purpose. They realize intensely that their interests are different from the disunity, from the antagonism felt and expressed by an overwhelming majority: those who are jealous of their own brethren: whose contempt, distrust or even hatred of all other men is one of the emotional sources of their life, one of the stimulants of their activity. These strange feelings are reinforced by what little historical knowledge they may have. Indeed historical learning and teaching has dealt thus far largely with the most obvious and noisy part of human evolution, but the least important. In spite of many appearances to the contrary, man's essential purpose is not a struggle for existence or for supremacy, not a devastating scramble for the goods of this world, but a generous and fruitful emulation in the creation and the diffusion of spiritual values. Now this creation takes place to a large extent secretly, for it is not accomplished by crowds, nor by pompous dignitaries officiating in the eyes of the people, but by individuals often poor and unknown, who carry on their sacred task in mean garrets, in wretched laboratories, or in other obscure corners scattered all over the civilized world, with hardly any regard for political boundaries, social or religious distinctions. "The wind bloweth where it listeth." The secrecy of their work is enhanced by the fact that it goes on in spite of the catastrophes, wars and revolutions which retain the whole attention of the people. Wars and revolutions are not essentially different from natural catastrophes such as earthquakes, volcanic eruptions, floods or epidemics; they are almost as impersonal and uncontrollable. For most men these catastrophes are by far the most important events, and this is natural enough, since their welfare is dreadfully affected by them. Galileo's or Newton's discoveries do not raise the price of food or shelter, at least not with sufficient suddenness to be perceptible. For us, on the contrary, these discoveries which must sooner or later transform man's outlook and, so to say, magnify both the universe and himself, are the cardinal events of the world's history. All the catastrophes, caused either by the untamed forces of nature or by the irrepressible folly of men, are nothing but accidents. They interrupt and upset man's essential activity but, however formidable, they do not and cannot dominate it.

The essential history of mankind is largely secret. Visible history is nothing but the local scenery, the everchanging and capricious background of this invisible history which, alone, is truly ecumenical and progressive. From our point of view, peoples and nations, even as men, are not to be judged by the power or the wealth they have attained, not by the amount of perishable goods which they produce, but only by their imperishable contributions to the whole of humanity.

5. LEONARDO AND THE BIRTH OF MODERN SCIENCE

1

Leonardo da Vinci died in the little manor of Cloux, near Amboise, where he had been for the previous three years the honored guest of Francis I, on May 2, 1519. He was not only one of the greatest artists, but even more the greatest scientist and the greatest engineer of his day. Indeed, with the passing of time his unique personality looms larger and larger and bids fair to attain, as soon as it is completely known, gigantic proportions.

Leonardo the artist is so well known that I shall hardly speak of him, but it is worth while for the purpose that I have in mind to recall briefly the most important facts of his life.

He was born in Vinci, a village in the hills between Florence and Pisa, in 1452, an illegitimate child, his mother being a peasant woman, and his father Ser Piero, a notary, a man of substance. The latter's family can be traced back to 1339, through three other generations of notaries. Soon after Leonardo's birth, his father took him away from his mother, and both parents hastened to marry, each in his own set. Ser Piero must have been a man of tremendous vitality, mental and physical. He was one of the most successful notaries of the Signoria and of the great families of Florence, and his wealth increased apace. He married four times, the two first unions remaining childless. His first legitimate child was not born until 1476, when Leonardo was already twenty-four, but after that ten more children were born to him by his third and fourth wives, the last one in the very year of his death, which occurred in 1504, when he was seventy-seven.

Thus Leonardo had five mothers. The real one disappears soon after his birth; she bore him and her mission ended there as far as Leonardo was concerned. What the four others were to him, we do not know, for he does not speak of them. He had five mothers and he had none. He is a motherless child, also a brotherless one, because he does not seem to have had much to do with his eleven brothers and sisters—far younger than himself anyhow —except when, at their father's death, they all leagued themselves against him to deny him any part of the patrimony. A motherless, brotherless, lonely childhood; we cannot lay too much stress on this; it accounts for so much.

In or about 1470 Ser Piero placed his son, now a very handsome and precocious boy, in the studio of Andrea Verrocchio, who since Donatello's death was the greatest sculptor of Florence; also a painter, a goldsmith, a very versatile man, indeed. Within the next years Leonardo had the opportunity to show the stuff of which he was made, and by 1480 his genius had matured. He was considered by common consent a great painter, and, moreover, his mind was swarming with ideas, not simply artistic ideas, but also architectural and engineering plans.

Leonardo was born in the neighborhood of Florence and bred in the great city. It is well, even in so short a sketch, to say what this implies. The people of Tuscany are made up of an extraordinary mixture of Etruscan, Roman, and Teutonic blood. Their main city, Florence, had been for centuries a considerable emporium, but also a center of arts and of letters. Suffice it to remember that of all the Italian dialects it is the Tuscan, and more specifically its Florentine variety, which has become the national language. The prosperous city soon took a lively interest in art, but loved it in its own way. These imaginative but cool-headed merchants patronize goldsmiths, sculptors, draftsmen. They do not waste any sentimentality, neither are they very sensual: clear outlines appeal more to them than gorgeous colors. Except when they are temporarily maddened by personal jealousy or by a feud which spreads like oil, it would be difficult to find people more level-headed, and having on an average more common sense and a clearer will.

Leonardo was a Florentine to the backbone, and yet this environment was not congenial to him. He was distinctly superior to most of his fellow citizens as a craftsman, but he could not match the best of them in literary matters. The Medici had gathered around them a circle of men whose delight it was to discuss topics of Greek, Latin, and vernacular literature, and to debate, often in a very learned manner, the subject of Platonic philosophy. There is no gainsaying that these Neoplatonists were a brilliant set of men, but their interests were chiefly of the literary kind; they were men of letters and loved beautiful discourse for its own sake. On the contrary, young Leonardo, following an irresistible trend, was carrying on scientific and technical investigations of every sort. The engineer in him was slowly developing. Perhaps, he could not help considering these amateur philosophers as idle talkers; but it is just as likely that, being a motherless child, he was not endowed with sufficient urbanity to fare comfortably in this society of refined dilettanti. Nature more and more engrossed his attention, and he was far more deeply concerned in solving its innumerable problems than in trying to reconcile Platonism and Christianity. Neither could his brother artists satisfy his intellectual needs; they were talking shop and fretting all the time. A few had shown some interest in scientific matters, but on the whole their horizon was too narrow and their self-centeredness unbearable. Also, Florence was becoming a very old place, and an overgrowth of traditions and conventions gradually crowded out all initiative and real originality. So Leonardo left and went to Milan, to the court of Ludovico Sforza, at that time one of the most splendid courts of Europe. Milan would certainly offer more opportunities to an enterprising and restless mind like his. The very desire of outdoing Florence was a tremendous impulse for Ludovico: he was anxious to make of his capital a new Athens, and of the near-by university town of Pavia a great cultural center. His happiest thought perhaps was to keep around him two men who were among the greatest of their day—Bramante and Leonardo. The liberal opportunities which were offered to these two giants are the supreme glory of the Sforzas and of Milan.

Leonardo was employed by the Duke as a civil and military engineer, as a pageant master, as a sculptor, as a painter, as an architect. How far he was understood by his patron it is difficult to say. But he seems to have thrived in this new atmosphere, and these Milanese years are among the most active and the most fertile of his life. He was now at the height of his power and full scope was given to his devouring activity. It is during this period, for instance, that he modelled his famous equestrian statue of Francesco Sforza, that he painted the "Virgin of the Rocks," and the "Last Supper," while he was also superintending important hydraulic works, and pursuing indefatigably his various scientific investigations. Yet even at this time of greatest activity and enthusiasm he must have been a lonesome man. This brilliant but very corrupt court was of course the rendezvous of hundreds of dilettanti, parasites, snobs—male and female—and what could Leonardo do to protect himself against them but be silent and withdraw into his own shell?

Milan justly shares with Florence the fame of having given Leonardo to the world; it was really his second birthplace. Unfortunately, before long, heavy clouds gathered over this joyous city, and by 1500 the show was over and Ludovico, made prisoner by the French, was to spend the last ten years of his life most miserably in the underground cell of a dungeon. From that time on, Leonardo's life became very unsettled. It is true, he spent many years in Florence, employed by the Signoria, painting "la Gioconda" and the "Battle of Anghiari"; then for some years he was back in Milan, but he is more and more restless and somehow the charm is broken. After the fall of the Sforzas, Isabella d'Este, Marchioness of Mantua—perhaps the most distinguished woman of the Renaissance—tried to attach Leonardo to her service, but he refused, and instead he chose, in 1502, to follow Cesare Borgia as his military engineer. One may wonder at this choice, yet it is easy enough to explain. At that time Leonardo was already far prouder of his achievements as a mechanic and an engineer than as a painter. It is likely that in the eyes of Isabella, however, he was simply an artist and he may have feared that this accomplished princess would give him but little scope for his engineering designs and his scientific research. On the other hand, Leonardo found himself less and less at home in Florence. The city had considerably changed in the last ten years. Savonarola had ruled it, and many of the artists had been deeply swayed by his passionate appeals, and even more by his death. For once, fair Florence had lost her head. And then also, young Michael Angelo had appeared, heroic but intolerant and immoderate: he and Leonardo were equally great but so different that they could not possibly get on together.

In 1513-15 Leonardo went to the papal court, but there, for the first time in his life, the old man was snubbed. Having left Rome, his prospects were getting darker, when fortunately he met in Bologna the young King of France, Francis I, who persuaded him to accept his patronage. The King offered him a little castle in Touraine, with a princely income, and there Leonardo spent in comparative quietness, the last three years of his life. It must be said to the credit of Francis I that he seems to have understood his guest, or at least to have divined his sterling worth. France, however, did not appreciate Leonardo, and was not faithful to her trust. The cloister of Saint-Florentin at Amboise, where the great artist had been buried, was destroyed by a fire in 1808, and his very ashes are lost.

He was apparently an old man when he died, much older than his years, exhausted by his relentless mind and by the vicissitudes and the miseries of his strange career. Only those who have known suffering and anxiety can fully understand the drama and the beauty of his life.

Throughout his existence Leonardo had carried on simultaneously, and almost without a break, his work as an artist, as a scientist, as an engineer. Such a diversity of gifts was not as unusual in his day as it would be now. Paolo Uccello, Leo B. Alberti, Piero dei Franceschi, even Verrocchio himself, had shown more than a casual interest in scientific matters such as perspective and anatomy, but Leonardo towers far above them. The excellence of his endowment is far more amazing than its complexity. His

curiosity was universal to such a degree that to write a complete
study of his genius amounts to writing a real encyclopædia of
fifteenth-century science and technology. From his earliest age he
had given proofs of this insatiable thirst for knowledge. He could
take nothing for granted. Everything that he saw, either in the
fields or on the moving surface of a river, or in the sky, or in the
bottega of his master, or in the workshops of Florence, raised a
new problem in his mind. Most of the time neither man nor book
could give an answer to his question, and his mind kept working
on it and remained restless until he had devised one himself. This
means, of course, that there was no rest for him until the end. In
a few cases, however, a satisfactory answer suggested itself, and
so a whole system of knowledge was slowly unfolding in him.

His apprenticeship in Verrocchio's studio must have greatly
fostered his inquiries in the theory of perspective, the art of light
and shade, and the physiology of vision; the preparation of colors
and varnishes must have turned his thoughts to chemistry; while
the routine of his work woke up naturally enough his interest in
anatomy. He could not long be satisfied by the study of the so-
called artistic anatomy, which deals only with the exterior
muscles. For one thing, the study of the movements of the human
figure, which he tried to express in his drawings, raised innumerable questions: how were they possible, what kept the human
machine moving and how did it work? . . . It is easy to
imagine how he was irresistibly driven step by step to investigate
every anatomical and physiological problem. There are in the
King's library at Windsor hundreds of drawings of his which
prove that he made a thorough analysis of practically all the
organs. Indeed, he had dissected quite a number of bodies, including that of a gravid woman, and his minute and comprehensive sketches are the first anatomical drawings worthy of the
name. Many of these sketches are devoted to the comparison of
human anatomy with the anatomy of animals, the monkey or the
horse for instance; or else he will compare similar parts of various
animals, say, the eyes or a leg and a wing. Other sketches relate

to pathological anatomy: the hardening of the arteries; tuberculous lesions of the lungs; a very searching study of the symptoms of senility.

On the other hand his activity as a practical engineer led him to study, or we might almost say to found, geology: he set to wonder at the various layers of sand and clay which the cutting of a canal did not fail to display; he tried to explain the fossils which he found embedded in the rocks and his explanations were substantially correct. Moreover, he clearly perceived the extreme slowness of most geological transformations, and figured that the alluvial deposits of the river Po were two hundred thousand years old. He well understood the geological action of water and its meteorological cycle.

His work as a sculptor, or as a military engineer (for instance, when he had to supervise the casting of bombards), caused him to study metallurgy, particularly the smelting and casting of bronze, the rolling, drawing, planing, and drilling of iron. On all these subjects he has left elaborate instructions and drawings. He undertook in various parts of northern Italy a vast amount of hydraulic work: digging of canals, for which he devised a whole range of excavating machines and tools; building of sluices; establishment of water wheels and pipes, and his study of hydrodynamics was so continuous that notes referring to it are found in all his manuscripts. He also studied the tides, but did not understand them.

In fact, it is impossible to give even a superficial account of all his scientific and technical investigations, and the reader must forgive me if the magnitude of the subject obliges me to limit myself to a sort of catalogue, for the adequate development of any single point would take many a page. Leonardo's manuscripts contain a great number of architectural drawings, sketches of churches and other buildings, but also more technical matters; he studied the proportion of arches, the construction of bridges and staircases; how to repair fissures in walls; how to lift up and move houses and churches. There is also much of what we would call town-

planning; the plague of Milan in 1484 likely was his great opportunity in this field, and he thought of various schemes to improve
public sanitation and convenience, including a two-level system
of streets. Botany repeatedly fixed his attention and we find many
notes on the life of plants, the mathematical distribution of leaves
on a stem, also beautiful and characteristic drawings of various
species. A great deal of the work undertaken for his employers
was of course connected with military engineering: hundreds of
notes and sketches on all sorts of arms and armor, on all imagin-
able offensive and defensive appliances; of course, many plans for
fortifications and strongholds (how to attack them and how to
defend them); portable bridges; mining and countermining;
tanks; various devices for the use of liquid fire, or of poisoning
and asphyxiating fumes. He adds occasional notes on military and
naval operations. He had even thought of some kind of submarine
apparatus, by means of which ships could be sunk, but the
dastardliness of the idea had horrified and stopped him.

No field, however, could offer a fuller scope to his prodigious
versatility and ingenuity than the one of practical mechanics. A
very intense industrial development had taken place in Tuscany
and Lombardy for centuries before Leonardo's birth; the prosperity of their workshops was greater than ever; there was a continuous demand for inventions of all kinds, and no environment
was more proper to enhance his mechanical genius.

Leonardo was a born mechanic. He had a deep understanding
of the elementary parts of which any machine, however complicated, is made up, and his keen sense of proportions stood him in
good stead when he started to build it. He devised machines for
almost every purpose which could be thought of in his day. I
quote a few examples at random: various types of lathes; machines
to shear cloth; automatic file-cutting machines; sprocket wheels
and chains for power transmission; machines to saw marble, to
raise water, to grind plane and concave mirrors, to dive under
water, to lift up, to heat, to light; paddle-wheels to move boats.
And mind you, Leonardo was never satisfied with the applications

alone, he wanted to understand as thoroughly as possible the principles underlying them. He clearly saw that practice and theory are twin sisters who must develop together, that theory without practice is senseless, and practice without theory hopeless. So it was not enough for him to hit upon a contrivance which answered his purpose; he wanted to know the cause of his success, or, as the case may be, of his failure. That is how we find in his papers the earliest systematic researches on such subjects as the stability of structures, the strength of materials, also on friction which he tried in various ways to overcome. That is not all: he seems to have grasped the principle of automaticity—that a machine is so much the more efficient, that it is more continuous and more independent of human attention. He had even conceived, in a special case, a judicious saving of human labor, that is, what we now call "scientific management."

His greatest achievement in the field of mechanics, however, and one which would be sufficient in itself to prove his extraordinary genius, is his exhaustive study of the problem of flying. It is complete, in so far that it would have been impossible to go further at his time, or indeed at any time until the progress of the automobile industry had developed a suitable motor. These investigations which occupied Leonardo throughout his life, were of two kinds. First, a study of the natural flying of birds and bats, and of the structure and function of their wings. He most clearly saw that the bird obtains from the air the recoil and the resistance which is necessary to elevate and carry itself forward. He observed how birds took advantage of the wind and how they used their wings, tails, and heads as propellers, balancers and rudders. In the second place, a mechanical study of various kinds of artificial wings, and of diverse apparatus by means of which a man might move them, using for instance the potential energy of springs, and others which he would employ to equilibrate his machine and steer its course.

It is necessary to insist that most of these drawings and notes of Leonardo's are not idle schemes, vague and easy suggestions such as we find, for instance, in the writings of Roger Bacon; but, on the contrary, very definite and clear ideas which could have been patented, if such a thing as a patent office had already existed! Moreover, a number of these drawings are so elaborate, giving us general views of the whole machine from different directions, and minute sketches of every single piece and of every detail of importance—that it would be easy enough to reconstruct it. In many cases, however, that is not even necessary, since these machines were actually constructed and used, some of them almost to our own time.

To visualize better the activity of his mind, let us take at random a few years of his life and watch him at work. We might take, for instance, those years of divine inspiration when he was painting the "Last Supper" in the refectory of Santa Maria delle Grazie, that is, about 1494-98. Do you suppose that this vast undertaking claimed the whole of his attention?

During these few years we see him act professionally as a pageant master, a decorator, an architect, an hydraulic engineer. His friend, Fra Luca Pacioli, the mathematician, tells us that by 1498 Leonardo "had completed with the greatest care his book on painting and on the movements of the human figure." We also know that before 1499, he had painted the portraits of Cecilia Gallerani and of Lucrezia Crivelli. Besides, his note-books of that period show that he was interested in a great variety of other subjects, chief among them hydraulics, flying, optics, dynamics, zoology, and the construction of various machines. He was also making a study of his own language, and preparing a sort of Italian dictionary. No wonder that the prior of Santa Maria complained of his slowness!

It so happened that during these four years he did not do much anatomical work, but during almost any other period he would have been carrying on some dissecting. Corpses were always hard to get, and I suppose that when he could get hold of one he made the most of it, working day and night as fast as he could. Then, as a change, he would go out into the fields and gaze at the stars, or at the earthshine which he could see inside the crescent of the moon; or else, if it were daytime, he would pick up fossils or marvel at the regularities of plant structure, or watch chicks breaking their shells. . . . Was it not uncanny? Fortunate was he to be born at a time of relative toleration. If he had appeared a century later, when religious fanaticism had been awakened, be sure this immoderate curiosity would have led him straight to the stake.

But remarkable as Leonardo's universality is, his earnestness and thoroughness are even more so. There is not a bit of dilettantism in him. If a problem has once arrested his attention, he will come back to it year after year. In some cases, we can actually follow his experiments and the hesitations and slow progress of his mind for a period of more than twenty-five years. That is not the least fascinating side of his notes; as he wrote them for his own private use, it is almost as if we heard him think, as if we were admitted to the secret laboratory where his discoveries were slowly maturing. Such an opportunity is unique in the history of science.

Just try to realize what it means: Here we have a man of considerable mother-wit, but unlearned, unsophisticated, who had to take up every question at the very beginning, like a child. Leonardo opened his eyes and looked straight upon the world. There were no books between nature and him; he was untrammelled by learning, prejudice, or convention. He just asked himself questions, made experiments and used his common sense. The world was one to him, and so was science, and so was art. But he did not lose himself in sterile contemplation, or in verbal generalities. He tried to solve patiently each little problem separately. He saw that the only fruitful way of doing that is first to state the problem as clearly as possible, then to isolate it, to make the necessary experiments and to discuss them. Experiment is always at the bottom; mathematics, that is, reason, at the end. In short, the method of inductive philosophy which Francis Bacon was to ex-

plain so well a century and a half later, Leonardo actually practiced.

This is, indeed, his greatest contribution: his method. He
deeply realized that if we are to know something of this world,
we can know it only by patient observation and tireless experiment. His note-books are just full of experiments and experimental
suggestions, "Try this . . . do that . . ." and we find also whole
series of experiments, wherein one condition and then another
are gradually varied. Now, that may seem of little account, yet it
is everything. We can count on our fingers the men who devised
real experiments before Leonardo, and these experiments are
very few in number and very simple.

But perhaps the best way to show how far he stood on the road
to progress, is to consider his attitude in regard to the many superstitions to which even the noblest and most emancipated minds of
his day paid homage, and which were to sway Europe for more
than two centuries after Leonardo's death. Just remember that in
1484, the Pope Boniface VIII had sown the seed of the witch
mania, and that this terrible madness was slowly incubating at the
time of which we are speaking. Now, Leonardo's contempt for
astrologers and alchemists was most outspoken and unconditional.
He met the spiritists of his age, as we do those of to-day, by
simply placing the burden of proof on their shoulders. It is true,
for all these matters, his Florentine ancestry stood him in good
stead. Petrarca had already shown how Florentine common sense
disposed of them; but Petrarca, man of letters, would not have
dared to treat the believers in ghosts, the medical quacks, the
necromancers, the searchers for gold and for perpetual motion as
one bunch of impostors. And that is what Leonardo did repeatedly
and most decidedly. Oh! how they must have liked him!

I must insist on this point: it is his ignorance which saved
Leonardo. I do not mean to say that he was entirely unlearned,
but he was sufficiently unlearned to be untrammelled. However
much he may have read in his mature years, I am convinced that

the literary studies of his youth were very poor. No teachers had time to mould his mind and to pervert his judgment. The good workman Verrocchio was perhaps his first philosopher, nature herself his real teacher. He was bred upon the experiments of the studio and of real life, not upon the artificialities of a mediæval library. He read more, later in life, but even then his readings, I think, were never exhaustive. He was far too original, too impatient. If he began to read, some idea would soon cross his mind, and divert his attention, and the book would be abandoned. Anyhow, at that time his mind was already proof against the scholastic fallacies; he was able, so to say, to filter through his own experience whatever mediæval philosophy reached him either in print or by word of mouth.

Neither do I mean to imply that all the schoolmen were dunces. Far from that, not a few were men of amazing genius, but their point of view was never free from prejudice; it was always the theological or legal point of view; they were always like lawyers pleading a cause; they were constitutionally unable to investigate a problem without reservation and without fear. Moreover, they were so cocksure, so dogmatic. Their world was a limited, a closed system; had they not encompassed and exhausted it in their learned encyclopædias? In fact they knew everything except their own ignorance.

Now the fact that Leonardo had been protected against them by his innocence is of course insufficient to account for his genius. Innocence is but a negative quality. Leonardo came to be what he was because he combined in himself a keen and candid intelligence with great technical experience and unusual craftsmanship. That is the very key to the mystery. Maybe if he had been simply a *theoretical* physicist, as were many of the schoolmen (their interest in astronomy and physics was intense), he would not have engaged in so many experiments. But as an engineer, a mechanic, a craftsman, he was experimenting all the while; he could not help it. If he had not experimented on nature, nature would have experimented on him; it was only a choice between offensive and defensive experimenting. Anyhow, whether he chose to take the initiative or not, these experiments were the fountainhead of his genius. To be sure, he had also a genuine interest in science, and the practical problems which he encountered progressively allured him to study it for its own sake, but that took time: once more the craftsman was the father of the scientist.

I would not have the reader believe that everything was wrong and dark in the Middle Ages. This childish view has long been exploded. The most wonderful craftsmanship inspired by noble ideals was the great redeeming feature of that period—unfortunately never applied outside the realm of religion and of beauty. The love of truth did not exalt mediæval craftsmen, and it is unlikely that the thought of placing his art at the service of truth ever occurred to any of them.

Now, one does not understand the Renaissance if one fails to see that the revolution—I almost wrote, the miracle—which happened at that time was essentially the application of this spirit of craftsmanship and experiment to the quest of truth, its sudden extension from the realm of beauty to the realm of science. That is exactly what Leonardo and his fellow investigators did. And there and then modern science was born, but unfortunately Leonardo remained silent, and its prophets came only a century later. . . .

Man has not yet found a better way to be truly original than to go back to nature and to disclose one of her secrets. The Renaissance would not have been a real revolution, if it had been simply a going back to the ancients; it was far more, it was a return to nature. The world, hitherto closed-in and pretty as the garden of a beguinage, suddenly opened into infinity. It gradually occurred to the people—to only very few at first—that the world was not closed and limited, but unlimited, living, forever becoming. The whole perspective of knowledge was upset, and as a natural consequence all moral and social values were transmuted. The humanists had paved the way, for the discovery of the classics had sharpened the critical sense of man, but the revolution itself could only be accomplished by the experimental philosophers. It is clear that the spirit of individuality, which is so often claimed to be the chief characteristic of this movement, is only one aspect of the experimental attitude.

It may seem strange that this technical basis of the Renaissance has been constantly overlooked, but that is simply due to the fact that our historians are literary people, having no interest whatever in craftsmanship. Even in art it is the idea and the ultimate result, not the process and the technique which engross their attention. Many of them look upon any kind of handicraft as something menial. Of course, this narrow view makes it impossible for them to grasp the essential unity of thought and technique, or of science and art. The scope of abstract thinking is very limited; if it be not constantly rejuvenated by contact with nature our mind soon turns in a circle and works in a vacuum. The fundamental vice of the schoolmen was their inability to avow that, however rich experimental premises may be, their contents are limited;—and there is no magic by means of which it is possible to extract from them more than they contain.

The fact that Leonardo's main contribution is the introduction, not of a system, but rather of a method, a point of view, caused his influence to be restricted to the few people who were not impervious to it. Of course, at almost any period of the past there have been some people—only a very few—who did not need any initiation to understand the experimental point of view, because their souls were naturally oriented in the right way. These men form, so to say, one great intellectual family: Aristotle, Archimedes, Ptolemy, Galen, Roger Bacon, Leonardo, Stevin, Gilbert, Galileo, Huygens, Newton. . . . They hardly need any incentive; they are all right anyhow. However, Leonardo's influence was even more restricted than theirs, because he could never prevail upon himself to publish the results of his experiments and meditations.

His notes show that he could occasionally write in a terse language and with a felicity of expression which would be a credit to any writer; but somehow he lacked that particular kind of moral energy which is necessary for a long composition, or he was perhaps inhibited, as so many scientists are, by his exacting ideal of accuracy.

All that we know of Leonardo's scientific activities is patiently dug out of his manuscripts. He was left-handed and wrote left-handedly, that is, in mirror-writing: his writing is like the image of ours in a mirror. It is a clear hand, but the disorder of the text is such that the reading is very painful. Leonardo jumps from one subject to another; the same page may contain remarks on dynamics, on astronomy, an anatomical sketch, and perhaps a draft and calculations for a machine.

The study of Dante is in many ways far simpler. His scientific lore does not begin to compare with Leonardo's knowledge. The *Divina Commedia* is the sublime apotheosis of the Middle Ages; Leonardo's note-books are not simply an epitome of the past, but they contain to a large extent the seeds of the future. The world of Dante was the closed mediæval world; the world of Leonardo is already the unlimited world of modern man: the immense vision which it opens is not simply one of beauty, of implicit faith, and of corresponding hope; it is a vision of truth, truth in the making. It is perhaps less pleasant, less hopeful; it does not even try to please, nor to give hope; it just tries to show things as they are: it is far more mysterious, and incomparably greater.

I do not mean to say that Dante had not loved truth, but he had loved it like a bashful suitor. Leonardo was like a conquering hero; his was not a passive love, but a devouring passion, an indefatigable and self-denying quest, to which his life and personal happiness were entirely sacrificed. Some literary people who do not realize what this quest implies, have said that he was selfish. It is true, he took no interest in the petty and hopeless political struggles of his day; Savonarola's revival hardly moved him, and he had no more use for religious charlatanry than for scientific quackery. One would be a poor man, however, who would not recognize at once in Leonardo's aphorisms a genuine religious feeling, that is, a deep sense of brotherhood and unity. His generosity, his spirit of detachment, even his melancholy, are unmistakable signs of true nobility. (He often makes me think of Pascal.) He was very lonely, of course, from his own choice, because he needed time and quietness, but also because, being so utterly different, it is easy to conceive that many did not like him. I find it hard to believe that he was very genial, in spite of what Vasari says. Being surrounded by people whose moral standards were rather low or, if these were higher, who were apt to lose their balance and to become hysterical because of their lack of knowledge, Leonardo's solitude could but increase, and to protect his equanimity he was obliged to envelop himself in a triple veil of patience, kindness, and irony.

Leonardo's greatest contribution was his method, his attitude; his masterpiece was his life. I have heard people foolishly regret that his insatiable curiosity had diverted him from his work as a painter. In the spiritual sphere it is only quality that matters. If he had painted more and roamed less along untrodden paths, his paintings perhaps would not have taught us more than do those of his Milanese disciples. While, even as they stand now, scarce and partly destroyed, they deliver to us a message which is so uncompromisingly high that even to-day but few understand it. Let us listen to it; it is worth while. This message is as pertinent and as urgent to-day as it was more than four hundred years ago. And should it not have become more convincing because of all the discoveries which have been made in the meanwhile? Do I dream, or do I actually hear, across these four centuries, Leonardo whisper: "To know is to love. Our first duty is to know. These people who always call me a painter annoy me. Of course, I was a painter, but I was also an engineer, a mechanic. My life was one long struggle with nature, to unravel her secrets and tame her wild forces to the purpose of man. They laughed at me because I was unlettered and slow of speech. Was I? Let me tell you: a literary education is no education. All the classics of the past cannot make men. Experience does, life does. They are rotten with learning and understand nothing. Why do they lie to themselves? How can they keep on living in the shade of knowledge, without coming out in the sun? How can they be satisfied with so little—when there is so much to be known, so much to be admired? . . . They love beauty, so they say—but beauty without truth is nothing but poison. Why do they not interrogate nature? Must we not first understand the laws of nature, and only then the laws and the conventionalities of men? Should we not give more importance to that which is most permanent? The study of nature is the substance of education—the rest is only the ornament. Study it with your brains and with your hands. Do not be afraid to touch her. Those who fear to experiment with their hands will never know anything. We must all be craftsmen of some kind. Honest craftsmanship is the hope of the world. . . ."

6. EVARISTE GALOIS

No episode in the history of thought is more moving than the life of Evariste Galois—the young Frenchman who passed like a meteor about 1828, devoted a few feverish years to the most intense meditation, and died in 1832 from a wound received in a duel, at the age of twenty. He was still a mere boy, yet within these short years he had accomplished enough to prove indubitably that he was one of the greatest mathematicians of all time. When one sees how terribly fast this ardent soul, this wretched and tormented heart, were consumed, one can but think of the beautiful meteoric showers of a summer night. But this comparison is misleading, for the soul of Galois will burn on throughout the ages and be a perpetual flame of inspiration. His fame is incorruptible; indeed the apotheosis will become more and more splendid with the gradual increase of human knowledge.

No existence could be more tragic than his and the only one at all comparable to it is, strangely enough, that of another mathematician, fully his equal, the Norwegian Niels Henrik Abel, who died of consumption at twenty-six in 1829; that is, just when Galois was ready to take the torch from his hand and to run with it a little further. Abel had the inestimable privilege of living six years longer, and think of these years—not ordinary years of a humdrum existence, but six full years at the time that genius was ripe—six years of divine inspiration! What would not Galois have given us, if he had been granted six more such years at the climax of his life? But it is futile to ask such questions. Prophecies too are futile, yet a certain amount of anticipation of the future may be allowed, if one does not contravene the experience of the past. For example, it is safe to predict that Galois' fame can but wax, because of the fundamental nature of his work. While the inventors of important applications, whose practical value is obvious, receive quick recognition and often very substantial rewards, the discoverers of fundamental principles are not generally awarded much recompense. They often die misunderstood and unrewarded. But while the fame of the former is bound to wane as new processes supersede their own, the fame of the latter can but increase. Indeed the importance of each principle grows with the number and the value of its applications; for each new application is a new tribute to its worth. To put it more concretely, when we are very thirsty a juicy orange is more precious to us than an orange tree. Yet when the emergency has passed, we learn to value the tree more than any of its fruits; for each orange is an end in itself, while the tree represents the innumerable oranges of the future. The fame of Galois has a similar foundation; it is based upon the unlimited future. He well knew the pregnancy of his thoughts, yet they were even more far-reaching than he could possibly dream of. His complete works fill only sixty-one small pages: but a French geometer, publishing a large volume some forty years after Galois' death, declared that it was simply a commentary on the latter's discoveries. Since then, many more consequences have been deduced from Galois' fundamental ideas which have influenced the whole of mathematical philosophy. It is likely that when mathematicians of the future contemplate his personality at the distance of a few centuries, it will appear to them to be surrounded by the same halo of wonder as those of Euclid, Archimedes, Descartes and Newton.

Evariste Galois was born in Bourg-la-Reine, near Paris, on the 25th of October, 1811 in the very house in which his grandfather had lived and had founded a boys' school. This being one of the very few boarding schools not in the hands of the priests, the Revolution had much increased its prosperity. In the course of time, grandfather Galois had given it up to his younger son and soon after, the school had received from the imperial government a sort of official recognition. When Evariste was born, his father was thirty-six years of age. He had remained a real man of the eighteenth century, amiable and witty, clever at rhyming verses and writing playlets, and instinct with philosophy. He was the leader of liberalism in Bourg-la-Reine, and during the Hundred Days had been appointed its mayor. Strangely enough, after Waterloo he was still the mayor of the village. He took his oath to the King, and to be sure he kept it, yet he remained a liberal to the end of his days. One of his friends and neighbours, Thomas François Demante, a lawyer and judge, onetime professor in the Faculty of Law of Paris, was also a typical gentleman of the "ancien régime," but of a different style. He had given a very solid classical education not only to his sons but also to his daughters. None of these had been more deeply imbued with the examples of antiquity than Adelaïde-Marie who was to be Evariste's mother. Roman stoicism had sunk deep into her heart and given to it a virile temper. She was a good Christian, though more concerned with the ethical than with the mystical side of religion. An ardent imagination had colored her every virtue with passion. Many more people have been able to appreciate her character than her son's, for it was to be her sad fortune to survive him forty years. She was said to be generous to a fault and original to the point of queerness. There is no doubt that Evariste owed considerably more to her than to his father. Besides, until the age of eleven the little boy had no teacher but his mother.

In 1823, Evariste was sent to college in Paris. This college— Louis-le-Grand—was then a gloomy house, looking from the outside like a prison, but within aflame with life and passion. For heroic memories of the Revolution and the Empire had remained particularly vivid in this institution, which was indeed, under the clerical and reactionary regime of the Restoration, a hot-bed of liberalism. Love of learning and contempt of the Bourbons divided the hearts of the scholars. Since 1815 the discipline had been jeopardized over and over again by boyish rebellions, and Evariste was certainly a witness of, if not a partner in, those which took place soon after his arrival. The influence of such an impassioned atmosphere upon a lad freshly emancipated from his mother's care cannot be exaggerated. Nothing is more infectious than political passion, nothing more intoxicating than the love of freedom. It was certainly there and then that Evariste received his political initiation. It was the first crisis of his childhood.

At first he was a good student; it was only after a couple of years that his disgust at the regular studies became apparent. He was then in the second class (that is, the highest but one) and the headmaster suggested to his father that he should spend a second year in it, arguing that the boy's weak health and immaturity made it imperative. The child was not strong, but the headmaster had failed to discover the true source of his lassitude. His seeming indifference was due less to immaturity than to his mathematical precocity. He had read his books of geometry as easily as a novel, and the knowledge had remained firmly anchored in his mind. No sooner had he begun to study algebra than he read Lagrange's original memoirs. This extraordinary facility had been at first a revelation to himself, but as he grew more conscious of it, it became more difficult for him to curb his own domineering thought and to sacrifice it to the routine of class work. The rigid program of the college was to him like a bed of Procrustes, causing him unbearable torture without adequate compensation. But how could the headmaster and the teachers understand this? The double conflict within the child's mind and between the teachers and himself, as the knowledge of his power increased, was intensely dramatic. By 1827 it had reached a critical point. This might be called the second crisis of his childhood: his scientific initiation. His change of mood was observed by the family. Juvenile gaiety was suddenly replaced by concentration; his manners became stranger every day. A mad desire to march forward along the solitary path which he saw so distinctly, possessed him. His whole being, his every faculty was mobilized in this immense endeavor.

I cannot give a more vivid idea of the growing strife between this inspired boy and his uninspired teachers than by quoting a few extracts from the school reports:

1826-1827

This pupil, though a little queer in his manners, is very gentle and seems filled with innocence and good qualities. . . . He never knows a lesson badly: either he has not learned it at all or he knows it well. . . .

A little later:

This pupil, except for the last fortnight during which he has worked a little, has done his classwork only from fear of punishment. . . . His ambition, his originality—often affected—the queerness of his character keep him aloof from his companions.

1827-1828

Conduct rather good. A few thoughtless acts. Character of which I do not flatter myself I understand every trait; but I see a great deal of self-esteem dominating. I do not think he has any vicious inclination. His ability seems to me to be entirely beyond the average, with regard as much to literary studies as to mathematics. . . . He does not seem to lack religious feeling. His health is good but delicate.

Another professor says:

His facility, in which one is supposed to believe but of which I have not yet witnessed a single proof, will lead him nowhere: there is no trace in his tasks of anything but of queerness and negligence.

Another still:

Always busy with things which are not his business. Goes down every day.

Same year, but a little later:

Very bad conduct. Character rather secretive. Tries to be original. . . .

Does absolutely nothing for the class. The furor of mathematics possesses him. . . . He is losing his time here and does nothing but torment his masters and get himself harassed with punishments. He does not lack religious feeling; his health seems weak.

Later still:

Bad conduct, character difficult to define. Aims at originality. His talents are very distinguished; he might have done very well in "Rhétorique" if he had been willing to work, but swayed by his passion for mathematics, he has entirely neglected everything else. Hence he has made no progress whatever. . . . Seems to affect to do something different from what he should do. It is possibly to this purpose that he chatters so much. He protests against silence.

In his last year at the college, 1828-1829, he had at last found a teacher of mathematics who divined his genius and tried to encourage and to help him. This Mr. Richard, to whom one cannot be too grateful, wrote of him: "This student has a marked superiority over all his schoolmates. He works only at the highest parts of mathematics." You see the whole difference. Kind Mr. Richard did not complain that Evariste neglected his regular tasks, and, I imagine, often forgot to do the petty mathematical exercises which are indispensable to drill the average boy; he does not think it fair to insist on what Evariste does not do, but states what he does do: he is only concerned with the highest parts of mathematics. Unfortunately, the other teachers were less indulgent. For physics and chemistry, the note often repeated was: "Very absent-minded, no work whatever."

To show the sort of preoccupations which engrossed his mind: at the age of sixteen he believed that he had found a method of solving general equations of the fifth degree. One knows that before succeeding in proving the impossibility of such resolution, Abel had made the same mistake. Besides, Galois was already trying to realize the great dream of his boyhood: to enter the École Polytechnique. He was bold enough to prepare himself alone for the entrance examination as early as 1828—but failed. This failure was very bitter to him—the more so that he considered it as unfair. It is likely that it was not at all unfair, at least according to the accepted rules. Galois knew at one and the same time far more and far less than was necessary to enter Polytechnique; his extra knowledge could not compensate for his deficiencies, and examiners will never consider originality with favor. The next year he published his first paper, and sent his first communication to the Académie des Sciences. Unfortunately, the latter got lost through Cauchy's negligence. This embittered Galois even more. A second failure to enter Polytechnique seemed to be the climax of his misfortune, but a greater disaster was still in store for him. On July 2 of this same year, 1829, his father had been driven to commit suicide by the vicious attacks directed against him, the liberal mayor, by his political enemies. He took his life in the small apartment which he had in Paris, in the vicinity of Louis-le-Grand. As soon as his father's body reached the territory of Bourg-la-Reine, the inhabitants carried it on their shoulders, and the funeral was the occasion of disturbances in the village. This terrible blow, following many smaller miseries, left a very deep mark on Evariste's soul. His hatred of injustice became the more violent, in that he already believed himself to be a victim of it; his father's death incensed him, and developed his tendency to see injustice and baseness everywhere.

His repeated failures to be admitted to Polytechnique were to Galois a cause of intense disappointment. To appreciate his despair, one must realize that the École Polytechnique was then, not simply the highest mathematical school in France and the place where his genius would be most likely to find the sympathy it craved, it was also a daughter of the Revolution who had remained faithful to her origins in spite of all efforts of the government to curb her spirit of independence. The young Polytechnicians were the natural leaders of every political rebellion; liberalism was for them a matter of traditional duty. This house was thus twice sacred to Galois, and his failure to be accepted was a double misfortune. In 1829 he entered the École Normale, but he entered it as an exile from Polytechnique. It was all the more diffi-

cult for him to forget the object of his former ambition, because
the École Normale was then passing through the most languid
period of its existence. It was not even an independent institution,
but rather an extension of Louis-le-Grand. Every precaution had
been taken to ensure the loyalty of this school to the new regime.
Yet there, too, the main student body inclined toward liberalism,
though their convictions were very weak and passive as compared with the mood prevailing at Polytechnique; because of the
discipline and the spying methods to which they were submitted,
their aspirations had taken a more subdued and hypocritical form
only relieved once in a while by spasmodic upheavals. Evariste
suffered doubly, for his political desires were checked and his
mathematical ability remained unrecognized. Indeed he was easily
embarrassed at the blackboard, and made a poor impression upon
his teachers. It is quite possible that he did not try in the least to
improve this impression. His French biographer, P. Dupuy, very
clearly explains his attitude:

> There was in him a hardly disguised contempt for whosoever
> did not bow spontaneously and immediately before his superiority,
> a rebellion against a judgment which his conscience challenged
> beforehand and a sort of unhealthy pleasure in leading it further
> astray and in turning it entirely against himself. Indeed, it is fre-
> quently observed that those people who believe that they have
> most to complain of persecution could hardly do without it and,
> if need be, will provoke it. To pass oneself off for a fool is another
> way and not the least savory, of making fools of others.

It is clear that Galois' temper was not altogether amiable, yet
we should not judge him without making full allowance for the
terrible strain to which he was constantly submitted, the violent
conflicts which obscured his soul, the frightful solitude to which
fate had condemned him.

In the course of the ensuing year, he sent three more papers to
mathematical journals and a new memoir to the Académie. The
permanent secretary, Fourier, took it home with him, but died
before having examined it, and the memoir was not retrieved

from among his papers. Thus his second memoir was lost like the former. This was too much indeed and one will easily forgive the wretched boy if in his feverish mood he was inclined to believe that these repeated losses were not due to chance but to systematic persecution. He considered himself a victim of a bad social organization which ever sacrifices genius to mediocrity, and naturally enough he cursed the hated regime of oppression which had precipitated his father's death and against which the storm was gathering. We can well imagine his joy when he heard the first shots of the July Revolution! But alas! While the boys of Polytechnique were the very first in the fray, those of the École Normale were kept under lock and key by their faint-hearted director. It was only when the three glorious days of July were over and the fall of the Bourbons was accomplished that this opportunist let his students out and indeed placed them at the disposal of the provisional government! Never did Galois feel more bitterly that his life had been utterly spoiled by his failure to become an alumnus of his beloved Polytechnique.

In the meanwhile the summer holidays began and we do not know what happened to the boy in the interval. It must have been to him a new period of crisis, more acute than any of the previous ones. But before speaking of it let me say a last word about his scientific efforts, for it is probable that thereafter political passion obsessed his mind almost exclusively. At any rate it is certain that Evariste was in the possession of his general principles by the beginning of 1830, that is, at the age of eighteen, and that he fully knew their importance. The consciousness of his power and of the responsibility resulting from it increased the concentration and the gloominess of his mind to the danger point; the lack of recognition developed in him an excessive pride. By a strange aberration he did not trouble himself to write his memoirs with sufficient clearness to give the explanations which were the more necessary because his thoughts were more novel. What a pity that there was no understanding friend to whisper in his ear Descartes' wise admonition: "When you have to deal with transcendent questions, you must be transcendently clear." Instead of that, Galois enveloped his thought in additional secrecy by his efforts to attain greater conciseness, that coquetry of mathematicians.

It is intensely tragic that this boy already sufficiently harassed by the turmoil of his own thoughts, should have been thrown into the political turmoil of this revolutionary period. Endowed with a stronger constitution, he might have been able to cope with one such; but with the two, how could he—how could anyone do it? During the holidays he was probably pressed by his friend, Chevalier, to join the Saint-Simonists, but he declined, and preferred to join a secret society, less aristocratic and more in keeping with his republican aspirations—the "Société des amis du peuple." It was thus quite another man who re-entered the École Normale in the autumn of 1830. The great events of which he had been a witness had given to his mind a sort of artificial maturity. The revolution had opened to him a fresh source of disillusion, the deeper because the hopes of the first moment had been so sanguine. The government of Louis-Philippe had promptly crushed the more liberal tendencies; and the artisans of the new revolution, who had drawn their inspiration from the great events of 1789, soon discovered to their intense disgust that they had been fooled. Indeed under a more liberal guise, the same oppression, the same favoritism, the same corruption soon took place under Louis-Philippe as under Charles X. Moreover, nothing can be more demoralizing than a successful revolution (whatever it be) for those who, like Galois, were too generous to seek any personal advantage and too ingenuous not to believe implicitly in their party shibboleths. It is such a high fall from one's dearest ideal to the ugliest aspect of reality—and they could not help seeing around them the more practical and cynical revolutionaries eager for the quarry, and more disgusting still, the clever ones, who had kept quiet until they knew which side was gaining, and who now came out of their hiding places to fight over the spoils and make the most of the new regime. Political fermentation did not abate and the more democratic elements, which Galois had joined, became more and more disaffected and restless. The director of the École Normale had been obliged to restrain himself considerably to brook Galois' irregular conduct, his "laziness," his intractable temper; the boy's political attitude, and chiefly his undisguised contempt for the director's pusillanimity now increased the tension between them to the breaking point. The publication in the "Gazette des Écoles" of a letter of Galois' in which he scornfully criticized the director's tergiversations was but the last of many offenses. On December 9, he was invited to leave the school, and his expulsion was ratified by the Royal Council on January 3, 1831.

To support himself Galois announced that he would give a private course on higher algebra in the backshop of a bookseller, Mr. Caillot, 5 rue de la Sorbonne. I do not know whether this course, or how much of it, was actually delivered. A further scientific disappointment was reserved for him: a new copy of his second lost memoir had been communicated by him to the Académie; it was returned to him by Poisson, four months later, as being incomprehensible. There is no doubt that Galois was partly responsible for this, for he had taken no pains to explain himself clearly.

This was the last straw! Galois' academic career was entirely compromised, the bridges were burned, he plunged himself entirely into the political turmoil. He threw himself into it with his habitual fury and the characteristic intransigency of a mathematician; there was nothing left to conciliate him, no means to moderate his passion, and he soon reached the extreme limit of exaltation. He is said to have exclaimed: "If a corpse were needed to stir the people up, I would give mine." Thus on May 9, 1831, at the end of a political banquet, being intoxicated—not with wine but with the ardent conversation of an evening—he proposed a sarcastic toast to the King. He held his glass and an open knife in one hand and said simply: "To Louis-Philippe!" Of course he was soon arrested and sent to Ste. Pélagie. The lawyer persuaded him to maintain that he had actually said: "To Louis-Philippe, *if he betray*," and many witnesses affirmed that they had heard him utter the last words, though they were lost in the uproar. But Galois could not stand this lying and retracted it at the public trial. His attitude before the tribunal was ironical and provoking, yet the jury rendered a verdict of not proven and he was acquitted. He did not remain free very long. On the following Fourteenth of July, the government, fearing manifestations, decided to have him arrested as a preventive measure. He was given six months' imprisonment on the technical charge of carrying arms and wearing a military uniform, but he remained in Ste. Pélagie only until March 19 (or 16?), 1832, when he was sent to a convalescent home in the rue de Lourcine. A dreadful epidemic of cholera was then raging in Paris, and Galois' transfer had been determined by the poor state of his health. However, this proved to be his undoing.

He was now a prisoner on parole and took advantage of it to carry on an intrigue with a woman of whom we know nothing, but who was probably not very reputable ("une coquette de bas étage," says Raspail). Think of it! This was, as far as we know, his first love—and it was but one more tragedy on top of so many others. The poor boy who had declared in prison that he could love only a Cornelia or a Tarpeia * (we hear in this an echo of his mother's Roman ideal), gave himself to this new passion with his usual frenzy, only to find more bitterness at the end of it. His revulsion is lamentably expressed in a letter to Chevalier (May 25, 1832):

> . . . How to console oneself for having exhausted in one month the greatest source of happiness which is in man—of having exhausted it without happiness, without hope, being certain that one has drained it for life?
>
> Oh! come and preach peace after that! Come and ask men who suffer to take pity upon what is! Pity, never! Hatred, that is all. He who does not feel it deeply, this hatred of the present, cannot really have in him the love of the future. . . .

* He must have quoted Tarpeia by mistake.

One sees how his particular misery and his political grievances are sadly muddled in his tired head. And a little further in the same letter, in answer to a gentle warning by his friend:

> I like to doubt your cruel prophecy when you say that I shall not work any more. But I admit it is not without likelihood. To be a savant, I should need to be that alone. *My heart has revolted against my head.** I do not add as you do: It is a pity.

Can a more tragic confession be imagined? One realizes that there is no question here of a man possessing genius, but of genius possessing a man. A man? a mere boy, a fragile little body divided within itself by disproportionate forces, an undeveloped mind crushed mercilessly between the exaltation of scientific discovery and the exaltation of sentiment.

Four days later two men challenged him to a duel. The circumstances of this affair are, and will ever remain, very mysterious. According to Evariste's younger brother the duel was not fair. Evariste, weak as he was, had to deal with two ruffians hired to murder him. I find nothing to countenance this theory except that he was challenged by two men at once. At any rate, it is certain that the woman he had loved played a part in this fateful event. On the day preceding the duel, Evariste wrote three letters of which I translate one:

May 29, 1832.

Letter to all Republicans.

> I beg the patriots, my friends, not to reproach me for dying otherwise than for the country.
>
> I die the victim of an infamous coquette. My life is quenched in a miserable piece of gossip.
>
> Oh! why do I have to die for such a little thing, to die for something so contemptible!
>
> I take heaven to witness that it is only under compulsion that I have yielded to a provocation which I had tried to avert by all means.

---

* The italics are mine.

I repent having told a baleful truth to men who were so little
able to listen to it coolly. Yet I have told the truth. I take with me
to the grave a conscience free from lie, free from patriots' blood.
Good-bye! I had in me a great deal of life for the public good.
Forgiveness for those who killed me; they are of good faith.

E. GALOIS

Any comment could but detract from the pathos of this document. I will only remark that the last line, in which Galois ab-
solves his adversaries, destroys his brother's theory. It is simpler
to admit that his impetuosity, aggravated by female intrigue, had
placed him in an impossible position from which there was no
honorable issue, according to the standards of the time, but a
duel. Evariste was too much of a gentleman to try to evade the
issue, however trifling its causes might be; he was anxious to pay
the full price of his folly. That he well realized the tragedy of his
life is quite clear from the laconic post-scriptum of his second
letter: *Nitens lux, horrenda procella, tenebris æternis involuta.*
The last letter addressed to his friend, Auguste Chevalier, was a
sort of scientific testament. Its seven pages, hastily written, dated
at both ends, contain a summary of the discoveries which he had
been unable to develop. This statement is so concise and so full
that its significance could be understood only gradually as the
theories outlined by him were unfolded by others. It proves the
depth of his insight, for it anticipates discoveries of a much later
date. At the end of the letter, after requesting his friend to publish it and to ask Jacobi or Gauss to pronounce upon it, he added:
"After that, I hope some people will find it profitable to unravel
this mess. *Je t'embrasse avec effusion.*"—The first sentence is
rather scornful but not untrue and the greatest mathematicians of
the century have found it very profitable indeed to clear up
Galois' ideas.

The duel took place on the 30th in the early morning, and he
was grievously wounded by a shot in the abdomen. He was found
by a peasant who transported him at 9:30 to the Hôpital Cochin.
His younger brother—the only member of the family to be noti-

fied—came and stayed with him, and as he was crying, Evariste tried to console him, saying: "Do not cry. I need all my courage to die at twenty." While still fully conscious, he refused the assistance of a priest. In the evening peritonitis declared itself and he breathed his last at ten o'clock on the following morning.

His funeral, which strangely recalled that of his father, was attended by two to three thousand republicans, including deputations from various schools, and by a large number of police, for trouble was expected. But everything went off very calmly. Of course it was the patriot and the lover of freedom whom all these people meant to honor; little did they know that a day would come when this young political hero would be hailed as one of the greatest mathematicians of all time.

A life as short yet as full as the life of Galois is interesting not simply in itself but even more perhaps because of the light it throws upon the nature of genius. When a great work is the natural culmination of a long existence devoted to one persistent endeavor, it is sometimes difficult to say whether it is the fruit of genius or the fruit of patience. When genius evolves slowly it may be hard to distinguish from talent—but when it explodes suddenly, at the beginning and not at the end of life, or when we are at a loss to explain its intellectual genesis, we can but feel that we are in the sacred presence of something vastly superior to talent. When one is confronted with facts which cannot be explained in the ordinary way, is it not more scientific to admit our ignorance than to hide it behind faked explanations? Of course it is not necessary to introduce any mystical idea, but it is one's duty to acknowledge the mystery. When a work is really the fruit of genius, we cannot conceive that a man of talent might have done it "just as well" by taking the necessary pains. Pains alone will never do; neither is it simply a matter of jumping a little further, for it involves a synthetic process of a higher kind. I do not say that talent and genius are essentially different, but that they are of different orders of magnitude.

Galois' fateful existence helps one to understand Lowell's saying: "Talent is that which is in a man's power, genius is that in whose power man is." If Galois had been simply a mathematician of considerable ability, his life would have been far less tragic, for he could have used his mathematical talent for his own advancement and happiness; instead of which, the furor of mathematics —as one of his teachers said—possessed him and he had no alternative but absolute surrender to his destiny.

Lowell's aphorism is misleading, however, for it suggests that talent can be acquired, while genius cannot. But biological knowledge points to the conclusion that neither is really acquired, though both can be developed and to a certain extent corrected by education. Men of talent as well as men of genius are born, not made. Genius implies a much stronger force, less adaptable to environment, less tractable by education, and also far more exclusive and despotic. Its very intensity explains its frequent precocity. If the necessary opportunities do not arise, ordinary abilities may remain hidden indefinitely; but the stronger the abilities the smaller need the inducement be to awaken them. In the extreme case, the case of genius, the ability is so strong that, if need be, it will force its own outlet.

Thus it is that many of the greatest accomplishments of science, art and letters were conceived by very young men. In the field of mathematics, this precocity is particularly obvious. To speak only of the two men considered in this essay, Abel had barely reached the age of twenty-two and Galois was not yet twenty, perhaps not yet nineteen, when they made two of the most profound discoveries which have ever been made. In many other sciences and arts, technical apprenticeship may be too long to make such early discovery possible. In most cases, however, the judgment of Alfred de Vigny holds good. "What is a great life? It is a thought of youth wrought out in ripening years." The fundamental conception dawns at an early age—that is, it appears at the surface of one's consciousness as early as this is materially possible—but it is often so great that a long life of toil and abnegation is but too short to work it out. Of course at the beginning it may be very vague, so vague indeed that its host can hardly distinguish it himself from a passing fancy, and later may be unable to explain how it gradually took control of his activities and dominated his whole being. The cases of Abel and Galois are not essentially different from those contemplated by Alfred de Vigny, but the golden thoughts of their youth were wrought out in the ripening years of other people.

It is the precocity of genius which makes it so dramatic. When it takes an explosive form, as in the case of Galois, the frail carcass of a boy may be unable to resist the internal strain and it may be positively wrecked. On the other hand when genius develops more slowly, its host has time to mature, to adapt himself to his environment, to gather strength and experience. He learns to reconcile himself to the conditions which surround him, widely different as they are, from those of his dreams. He learns by and by that the great majority of men are rather unintelligent, uneducated, uninspired, and that one must not take it too much to heart when they behave in defiance of justice or even of common sense. He also learns to dissipate his vexation with a smile or a joke and to protect himself under a heavy cloak of kindness and humor. Poor Evariste had no time to learn all this. While his genius grew in him out of all proportion to his bodily strength, his experience and his wisdom, he felt more and more ill at ease. His increasing restlessness makes one think of that exhibited by people who are prey to a larvate form of a pernicious disease. There is an internal disharmony in both cases, though it is physiological in the latter, and psychological in the former. Hence the suffering, the distress and finally the acute disease or the revolt!

A more congenial environment might have saved Galois. Oh! would that he had been granted that minimum of understanding and sympathy which the most concentrated mind needs as much as a plant needs the sun! . . . But it was not to be; and not only had he no one to share his own burden, but he had also to bear the anxieties of a stormy time. I quite realize that this self-centered boy was not attractive—many would say not lovable. Yet I love

him; I love him for all those who failed to love him; I love him because of his adversity.

His tragic life teaches us at least one great lesson: one can never
be too kind to the young; one can never be too tolerant of their
faults, even of their intolerance. The pride and intolerance of
youth, however immoderate, are excusable because of youth's
ignorance, and also because one may hope that it is only a temporary disorder. Of course there will always be men despicable
enough to resort to snubbing, as it were, to protect their own position and to hide their mediocrity, but I am not thinking of them.
I am simply thinking of the many men who were unkind to Galois
without meaning to be so. To be sure, one could hardly expect
them to divine the presence of genius in an awkward boy. But
even if they did not believe in him, could they not have shown
more forbearance? Even if he had been a conceited dunce, instead
of a genius, could kindness have harmed him? . . . It is painful
to think that a few rays of generosity from the heart of his elders
might have saved this boy or at least might have sweetened his
life.

But does it really matter? A few years more or less, a little more
or less suffering. . . . Life is such a short drive altogether. Galois
has accomplished his task and very few men will ever accomplish
more. He has conquered the purest kind of immortality. As he
wrote to his friends: "I take with me to the grave a conscience
free from lie, free from partiots' blood." How many of the conventional heroes of history, how many of the kings, captains and
statesmen could say the same?

7. ERNEST RENAN

I am writing in Ogunquit, one of the loveliest towns on the shores of Maine, but my imagination takes me back to the other side of the Atlantic, to the rude coast of Brittany, somewhere between Saint Brieux and Roscoff. There are of course many points of comparison between the shores of Maine and the Côtes du Nord, but they are more generally a matter of contrast than of resemblance. This side of the Atlantic is very gentle as compared with the Emerald Coast, the rugged, the fantastic, the awful defences of Brittany against a turbulent sea. Why then does my mind carry me thither? Reminiscences of a sentimental journey which I accomplished years ago might account for it, but the true reason is that having been imprisoned in my study for many days by the inclemency of the weather, I read or reread books of Renan's. Oh, the magic of this beautiful language, so melodious yet so simple and so direct that it reminds me—as no other ever did—of the best Greek prose, of the winged words of a Plato or a Xenophon! While I was reading I heard the song of the birds, the chirping of the crickets, the buzzing of other insects, and farther off the deep voice of the sea; and all of that intensified the music of his language and the rhythm of my joy. Thus when my eyes gaze over the blue water, when I smell at ebb-tide the acrid odor of seaweed, my mind flies back to that place across the mighty ocean, where Renan was born and spent his boyhood—Tréguier—and to that old manor of Rosmapamon and the little fishermen's village, Perros-Guirec, where he lived his last summer and dreamed his last dreams.

Ernest Renan was born on the 27th of February, 1823, in the old town of Tréguier, one of those dead cities of Brittany, where there is so little bustle that one can almost hear the people muse and pray in the empty streets. He was a seven-month baby, extremely frail, and for a while it was thought that he would not survive. But for a maternal grandfather hailing from Bordeaux, he was a pure Celt, and this means a great deal. These people of Brittany, however devoted they may be to their foster country, are very different from the ordinary Frenchman—at least as much as a Welshman or an Irishman is different from your average Englishman. Their idiosyncrasies are deeply rooted in the past. For one thing, those out-of-the-way provinces of the West were hardly touched by the Roman colonization; they pursued undisturbed their own development and such was their originality and their sturdiness that the most zealous propaganda of the gospel could not eradicate entirely their pagan beliefs; the Christian evangelists who came to minister to them were forced in many cases to close their eyes to older superstitions and compromise with them as best they might. Renan realized this very strongly as soon as he reached Paris, and even more when he first visited Athens in 1865. On that occasion he expressed the strange qualities of his native soil very strikingly in the prayer to Athena "which he made on the Acropolis when he had finally reached a proper understanding of its perfect beauty":

"O nobility! O beauty simple and true! Goddess whose cult means reason and wisdom, thou whose temple is an eternal lesson of conscience and sincerity: I bring to thine altar much remorse. To find thee cost me infinite research. The initiation which thou didst bestow upon the Athenian at his birth, in one smile, I have conquered only by strength of reflection, at the price of long efforts.

"I was born, blue-eyed goddess, of barbarian parents among the kind and virtuous Cimmerians who live at the edge of a dark sea, bristling with rocks, ever beaten by storms. The sun is scarcely known there; our flowers are marine mosses, seaweeds and the colored shells which one finds tossed up in the lonely bays. The clouds there seem to be without color, and joy itself takes on a tinge of sadness, but springs of cold water burst from the rocks and the eyes of our young girls are like those green springs wherein the sky is mirrored over undulating grasses. . . ."

His father was a sea captain who, in his old age, in unwise commercial ventures had lost the savings of a laborious life. When he died at sea rather mysteriously in 1828, his widow was left with hardly any property and two children: Henriette, aged seventeen, and little Ernest, twelve years younger. But Henriette saved the family; her little earnings as a teacher and later as a governess in a Polish castle, made it possible to give her brother the best opportunities. It had been taken for granted that he would become a priest; his intelligence and gentleness, his lack of strength, his poverty and the traditions of his family did not seem to leave any alternative. He received his first education in the excellent cathedral school of Tréguier, and achieved so much success that he was called in 1838 to the seminary of St. Nicolas du Chardonnet in Paris, then in the process of reorganization. Four industrious years at Saint Nicolas promoted one generally to the greater seminary of Saint Sulpice to work on higher studies. The first year was devoted chiefly to philosophy and that teaching took place, not in the main house, but in a country mansion located in Issy, near Vaugirard. This was a beautiful residence which had been inhabited at the beginning of the seventeenth century by Margaret of Valois, the first wife of Henry IV. It had kept much of its old-fashioned elegance and dignity. The park was particularly graceful and Renan spent much of his time in it, sitting on a stone bench in one of the long alleys, reading indefatigably and meditating to his heart's content. He said later that this park had been, after the cathedral of Tréguier, the second cradle of his thought; he could never see an arbor or a hedge of yoke-elms cut in the conventional manner of his country, nor smell damp leaves in the autumn, without remembering his long and melancholy meditations of Issy. In 1843 he was finally admitted into the main house of Saint Sulpice in Paris, and there he spent three fruitful years studying more theology, but also Hebrew and Syriac.

It was during these last school years that he resolved to devote his life to the study of the origins of Christianity, but his philo-

logical research made it more and more difficult for him to accept
implicitly the dogmas which had been hitherto the fixed stars of
his thought. At first he had been troubled only by metaphysical
difficulties, but such can be evaded, or at least one may nourish
the illusion of evading them; the study of the original texts now
revealed to him the existence of inadvertencies, errors and contradictions which could not be denied. Neither did the dating of
those sacred documents by means of scientific methods tally at all
with the traditional chronology. Once these hard facts had been
faced, there was no honest way of shunning them, and his conscience was a prey to unremitting distress. For a while, however,
he hoped against all hope that it would remain possible to reconcile the facts with his faith; and maybe he would have suc-
cumbed to his intense desire for such reconciliation, to his passionate love of the church in which he had been brought up, to
his fear of saddening the hearts of his teachers and of his beloved
mother; he might have succeeded in persuading himself that it
was his duty to silence the doubts of his mind and to follow the
road which traditions of his family, his own inclinations and fate
itself had traced for him from the beginning. Men, even the best
of them, are only too often tempted to sacrifice the essential duty
of their lives to some immediate duty, the importance of which is
more tangible. Happily at this critical juncture, at this parting of
the ways, Ernest received the assistance of his sister. Henriette
was then tutoring in Poland, but there was a close correspond-
ence between them; partly because of her age and experience,
partly because of her greater decision and the simplicity of her
character, she saw more clearly than her brother his main duty:
there can be no compromise with truth as one sees it; to evade
the dictates of one's conscience on a matter of fundamental importance is cowardice, however generous the reasons for such
evasions be. She did not simply offer him spiritual assistance, but
placed at his disposal her humble savings, some twelve hundred
francs, which would enable him to face the first necessities with
less anxiety. It would be futile to imagine what his course would

have been without his sister's help; at any rate her unparalleled
courage and devotion made it much easier for him to do the only
thing which was completely honest. On the 6th of October, 1845,
he left Saint Sulpice, wearing for the last time the cassock of a
seminarist.

It must be said that his masters respected his decision and did
not cease, at least for some time, to be his friends; they had had
many opportunities to test the purity of his heart and they well
knew that there was in it neither revolt nor sensuality, but the
most genuine and intense religion. On the other hand, he himself
always spoke with the highest appreciation of the education
which they had imparted to him. Saint Sulpice in Renan's day
(and perhaps even now) was essentially a seventeenth-century
institution; nothing could remind one more of Port Royal or the
old Sorbonne than did this college where time seemed to have
stood still. The studies were extremely serious; there was a
healthy amount of freedom; the moral tone was the highest. The
theological teaching was rigorously honest. Some at least of his
teachers would have been the last, knowing the doubts preying on
his mind, to let him tie himself forever by a half-hearted taking of
sacred vows. They did not try in the least to make proselytes by
means of equivocations or to dispose of dogmatic difficulties or
textual contradictions by sleight-of-hand. They acted according to
the truth as they saw it, and Renan did nothing but follow their
admonitions, though the light which he saw was more distant and
drew him reluctantly far away from them. He was especially
grateful to his teacher of Semitic languages, and said of him: "All
that I am as a savant, I owe to M. Le Hir. I sometimes think that
I have never known well the things that I learned without him.
For example, he was not very strong in Arabic, and therefore I
have always remained a mediocre Arabist." But his thankfulness
was extended to the whole school and when later he reviewed his
life in Marcus Aurelius' manner, trying to determine the various
influences which had moulded it, he recognized that Saint Sulpice
had been by far the principal factor. The moral education of that

great seminary had imbued his whole substance, and his anxious love for those from whom his conscience had obliged him to part caused him to declare (with some exaggeration) : "Since I left Saint Sulpice I have done nothing but decline, and yet with but one quarter of a Sulpician's virtues, I have still been, I believe, far above the average."

Nothing can be harder than to break with the faith of one's youth, with the traditions of one's people, with the ideals of one's teachers. Though Renan had taken no final vows, when he left Saint Sulpice on that fateful October day, he must have felt like an apostate. He was leaving a house which had been for him a second home and found himself alone and poor, without friends (except those he was deserting), in a cold and indifferent world. Dark days followed, days of solitude and trial, which might have become unendurable but for the clear purpose which guided his mind like a star in the night. Then fate was kind to him. For the next month the hands of a new friend were stretched out to him, and before long they helped and enabled him to evoke a new and greater vision.

This friend, four years younger than himself, was a student of science, Marcellin Berthelot, who became eventually one of the leading chemists of the century. He was fully Renan's equal both from the intellectual and the moral point of view, and, so to say, his complement in the matter of knowledge. At the time of their meeting, Renan's erudition was already considerable, but was restricted to the philosophical, historical and literary disciplines, while Berthelot had devoted most of his attention to the experimental sciences. Their political opinions were just as divergent, for Renan was a tory and a monarchist, while his friend was a liberal and a republican (the first republican Renan had ever met!). However, their love of knowledge was equally intense; they were animated by the same idealism, the same respect for human reason; and, though the great tasks to which they had already dedicated their young lives were very different, they were sustained by the same heroic devotion to them. Such a friendship

was at once a great source of happiness and an incomparable
opportunity. I like to imagine these two youths discussing together, with equal candor and passion, either in Renan's garret
or else in the quieter streets of the "Quartier Latin." The conflicts
of their points of view, the clashes of their enthusiasms, the piec-
ing together of their information, the continual challenge of their
respective prejudices could but be immensely fruitful. They discussed endlessly every problem of life; and, as one of them remarked, "Social and philosophic questions must be very difficult
indeed that we were not able to solve them in our desperate
effort!"

The two friends weathered together the Revolution of 1848,
and the result of their incessant colloquies during that tremendous
crisis was a book which, although written by Renan, bore traces
of Berthelot's influence on almost every page: *The Future of
Science*. It was at once a social survey, a sort of general introduction to scientific studies, an attempt to establish a general philosophy exclusively upon the data of experience, above all an impassioned appeal to apply scientific methods to the solution of
social and political issues. It was chaotic to a degree and as dogmatic and naive as we might expect the encyclopedic treatise of
any young man to be. Crude, aggressive, tactless, poorly written
(as it was) it was nevertheless full of excellent suggestions cleverly
made, full of delicious remarks, full of learning and wisdom.
Neither should we forget that much in it which may seem com-
monplace to-day was relatively new in 1848; indeed, some parts
—signally his insistence that philosophy should be based on positive knowledge—are not yet generally understood. A careful analysis of it would show that it contained the germs of the best
thoughts of his maturity, and we could easily find in it a raw
delineation of his later attitude. Though he was fully aware of
the crudities and shortcomings of this maiden work, Renan never
disavowed its main substance. Indeed, when his first revulsion
against it, caused by his Italian journey, was softened, throughout
his life he retained a tender feeling for it and used to call it affec-

tionately his old Purana. Towards the end of his life he had the
courage (or the weakness) to publish it in full without any
change. Such a book is tremendously interesting; not so much as
an achievement, however, as a promise. It could but be pleasant
for the old man when he reread these lucubrations of his youth
to realize not only that he had fully kept his promise, but also
that the world had moved—in the main—along the lines he had
foreseen.

Berthelot's influence upon the development of Renan's thought
can not be overestimated. They remained to the last a unique pair
of friends. Theirs was a sort of sacred union, excluding any familiarity or indulgence, which must have seemed inhuman to those
who were not actuated by the same earnest conception of life,
the same absolute devotion to a great duty, the same inveterate
habit of considering all things from the point of view of eternity.
They were two young heroes walking along different paths to a
single aim; their quests, however distinct to all appearances, were
essentially the same. They wanted to increase the light and to
dissipate the clouds of darkness—and their enemy was also the
same dragon with a hundred heads, unreason, credulity, superstition, intolerance. . . .

The voyage to Italy which Renan made in 1849-50 is very important because it was his artistic initiation. It brought suddenly
to the surface of his soul the love of beauty which had been stifled
by his immoderate studies and was almost buried under a tremendous load of knowledge. It mellowed his thought and made
him realize that he too was an artist. His first published work—
his *Averroës*—which appeared a couple of years later shows the
progress that he had made in every respect. It is the fruit of a mature mind which has found out that the duty of a writer is less
to exhibit the sum of his knowledge than to deliver his message,
the work of one who has learned the art of composing his thoughts
and pruning his style, who has taken the trouble to recast his ideas
until their form be as simple and elegant as possible. In fact, this

Averroës, written before he was thirty, has remained a classic of philosophic literature.

The artistic development of the young author was considerably hastened by his acquaintance with the Dutch painter Ary Scheffer, whose niece Cornelie he married in or about 1854. Since Henriette's return from Poland, she had been living with her brother. She now joined the young couple and became a warm friend of the bride and later of their children, Ary and Ernestine. A little later, Ernest's old mother joined them too. He had now to provide for a large family, and it was sometimes difficult to keep the wolf from the door. He wrote articles for the *Revue des Deux Mondes* and the *Journal des Débats*, and was employed in the Department of Manuscripts of the National Library, but all that hardly sufficed to keep such a large pot boiling. In 1857 the chair of Hebrew at the Collège de France became vacant by the death of Quatremère. Renan was the one man in France qualified to occupy it (he had published in 1855 his *General History of Semitic Languages* and was already a member of the Institut), but religious prejudice blocked the way to his nomination. The injustice done to him was so flagrant, however, that the government entrusted to him—as a sort of compensation—a scientific mission to ancient Phoenicia. Nothing more fortunate could have happened to him. This long voyage in the Near East completed his artistic initiation and gave him the archaeological and pictorial background which he needed to write to his satisfaction the first volumes of the *Origins of Christianity*. The devoted Henriette accompanied him, acting as his manager, his secretary and his beloved confidante. They travelled extensively in Palestine, visiting together—one can easily imagine with what passion—all the places hallowed by one of the greatest dramas of history. Unfortunately the hot and damp climate of the Syrian coast had told upon their health, especially upon Henriette who was very far from strong. Her condition soon reached such a critical stage that they decided to move into the hills and to settle in Ghazir, at the end of the Bay of Kesruan, one of the most beautiful spots in the world. It is there that Renan began the composition of his *Life of Jesus*. But the move had been too late; and in September 1861 a malignant fever laid them low and carried off Henriette. She had given the most perfect example of sisterly devotion; and it would be unfair to think of him, whom she loved so well, without thinking also of her. She is buried under the palm trees of Amschitt, and our grateful thoughts linger there with her. Renan came back from Palestine with the sketch of a masterpiece, but he had paid a heavy price for it.

The *Vie de Jésus* appeared in 1863. Its success was immense. Some of it, to be sure, was of a sensational nature. There was so much in that lofty book to shock and enrage the bigots that they could not ignore it. Its success, however, was due to a far greater extent to the warm sympathy which it aroused. Renan had spoken straight to the hearts of men and they had responded. From that time on, his fame as a writer was so solidly established that his livelihood was relatively secure. Oh! that Henriette had been able to share his triumph and his comfort! The heroic years were over—after all, those were the best, and she had shared them fully. There remained thirty more years which his indefatigable activity filled to the brim, but the recital of such activity lacks interest. His was the retired life of a savant, outwardly monotonous, though inwardly so full and so rich, periodically interrupted by vacations in diverse parts of Europe. If one were telling the life of a third-rate personality one would make capital of such voyages; one would narrate them at great length as if they were journeys of discovery; one would draw the reader's attention to every distinguished man whom one's hero met as if to divert a little of their brilliance to him. But when the traveller is himself a great personality, whose brightness is not borrowed but original; when he travels not to gratify an aimless curiosity or a despicable snobbishness, but to recreate his mind, to attain a fresh point of view, to find material for his work and food for his thought, such stories become pointless. At least the history of his movements is so inextricably mixed with that of his own mind that it is not possible to separate one from the other. Now, to explain the development of his mind would oblige me to analyze his works in their natural sequence, and I do not propose to do so. The only one of his many books which it would be unpardonable not to mention is his *Souvenirs d'Enfance et de Jeunesse,* one of the most charming pieces of autobiography which has ever been written. The French people gave this little book the most enthusiastic welcome—a welcome which they had never given before to a book of the same kind, except perhaps to the *Mémoires d'Outre-Tombe.* I suppose Renan wrote it during one of his vacations in his native province, when his growing age and failing health discouraged longer journeys and when nostalgia drew him back to the haunts of his boyhood. At least, when I read those pages, I seem to hear the sea-voices of Brittany and smell the goémon. Here is told the story of his intellectual development to the time of the great crisis of his life, his departure from Saint Sulpice, but a few digressions carry the tale a little farther. The tone is familiar and the reminiscences are not complete but fragmentary, yet they offer us in an exquisite form the essential facts of his growth, the facts which he alone could tell us; the rest might as well be told by others or left untold. For with few exceptions (and Renan was not one of them) the fate of any great writer, scientist or artist has been largely determined before he was thirty. The initial struggle is the thing, not the victory.

Renan died in Paris in October 1892. The work in which he himself took most pride was his edition, together with two colleagues of the Institut, of the whole body of Semitic inscriptions; this great undertaking placed within the reach of the few scholars interested in it, the fundamental materials wherewith to rebuild the past with greater accuracy. However, he will be chiefly remembered, among a large élite, by his noble efforts to purify the religious spirit, by his conception of history and philosophy as scientific disciplines, by his broad humanism and, last but not least, by the charm and the unaffected elegance, the simplicity, the perfect cadence of his prose. He was one of the leading philosophers among the historians of the last century and one of the greatest literary artists.

The most characteristic trait of Renan's thought is his scientific conception of history and, conversely, his rare understanding of the spirit of positive science. To be sure this was largely due to his constant intercourse with Marcellin Berthelot, but the latter's influence would have been of little avail if Renan had not been fully prepared to receive it. When he exclaims in one of his prefaces to the *Life of Jesus*, "History is a science like chemistry, like geology," there comes to us an echo of their discussions on the subject. Renan, whose sole knowledge was historical, had been suddenly brought face to face with a man whose conceptions and ideals, though strangely similar to his own, were based on an altogether different set of facts. On the other hand Berthelot had probably been led to believe—as most young scientists are—that there was no real knowledge outside the field of the positive or experimental sciences, and we may expect him to have taken pains to impress his theological companion with this conviction. The test of knowledge, he might say, is the ability to foresee, to bring about definite results with certainty. The experimental sciences are the only ones which make such knowledge possible. Of course Renan could not share such an intolerant conception, but he would learn to understand the pure scientific point of view, as no other historian ever did. Thus, after having reviewed the intellectual conditions of Islam, he concludes, "The purpose of mankind is not repose in submissive ignorance, but implacable war against error and struggle against evil. Science is the soul of society for science is reason . . . It creates military and industrial superiority. It will some day create social superiority; I mean a state of society wherein the full amount of justice compatible with the essence of the universe will be available." Berthelot would have expressed himself exactly in the same way, but he would have stopped there. Renan was not inclined to throw overboard as worthless his own treasure of facts, to the collection of which he had devoted so many years of intense study. He realized keenly that there was an immense field of knowledge to which the methods of positive science could not yet be applied—and maybe could never be; but that was no reason to give up its exploration as hopeless. The duty in every case remained the same: to find as much of the truth as possible. If but little truth could be attained with certainty, it was nevertheless one's duty to find that little. The science of the human mind is essentially historical, for all that we do, all that we know, all that we are is the result of ageless labor and immemorial experience. The best way to understand the development of our mind and to fathom its nature and possibilities is to study the history of mankind—to study it with the same scrupulous accuracy with which the naturalist seeks to unravel the succession of geologic or biologic changes. Renan understood all this very clearly and his philosophy was completed by a vague concept of evolution as a universal law of life.

The idea of evolution was of course in the air, and the tumult and disruptions of 1848 had done much to replace in the popular mind the general notions of tradition and immobility by that of ceaseless change. Dynamical or historical explanations were everywhere substituted for the merely static—for the dogmatic descriptions of an immobile reality. It is interesting to note that Spencer and Darwin were thinking on this very subject at the same time as Renan—it must be admitted with far greater depth—but his contribution is nevertheless of great importance, for it came from the other pole of research.

Renan's scientific attitude is best illustrated by his love of concrete facts and his distrust of premature generalizations. Thus he would say, "Reason alone cannot create truth . . . The attempt to construct a theory of things by the play of empty formulas is as vain a pretense as that of the weaver who would produce linen without putting any thread in his shuttle," and again, "It is philology or erudition which will provide the thinker with that forest of things (*silva rerum ac sententiarum*, as Cicero puts it), without which philosophy will never be more than a

Penelope's weaving always to be recommenced." This was partly a revulsion against the theological arguments of his youth, partly a natural impulse intensified by Berthelot's example.

I speak of natural impulse advisedly, for it is obvious that Renan was a born scientist. The fundamental qualities of a true scientist were genuine parts of his substance; the love of truth, of accuracy, and even more the disinterestedness and the courage without which this love is easily stifled at the very time when it is most needed.

This leads us to examine his religion, a subject it is far easier to discuss now than in his own time, when some fanatics went so far as to consider him as a sort of Antichrist. The core of his religion, which was intense, was this very love of truth. One might be tempted to ask, is it possible that religion be based on something else? But it is wiser to ask no such question; for it would oblige us to deny the religion of a large number of people who consider themselves, in perfect good faith, as deeply religious, though they have no idea of truth, no means of recognizing it, no love of it, no use for it. Their religion is irrational, but we cannot say that it is not genuine.

Aside from this love of truth which remained the absorbing passion of his life, Renan had retained from his early education a double imprint; the conviction of the necessity of a moral aristocracy, and the feeling that such aristocracy was essentially one of service, enjoying no privilege but to be what it was and expecting no other, not even the privilege of wide recognition. According to him, the truly inferior men are the great mass of the self-centered, snobbish and stupid people, who have no other motives than the improvement of their position, the furthering of their own petty interests. On the contrary, the true mark of the aristocracy—in which he had placed all his hope of moral progress—is its disinterestedness, its eagerness to devote itself to the community without the thought of any reward. He insisted repeatedly in every one of his writings on the essential importance of such disinterestedness. The purpose of man, as far as we can understand it, is to create intellectual values, that is, to produce beautiful things, to discover and vindicate truth, to increase justice and human solidarity. Every disinterested effort in that direction, however humble, is a positive gain, however small, for the whole world. To put it in the simplest terms, he who takes life earnestly and forgets himself is, to that extent, religious; he who is frivolous, self-complacent, superficial, selfish, is, to that extent, irreligious.

When Renan renounced the taking of the sacred orders to devote himself entirely to scholarly pursuits, the change appeared to the bigots immense, abysmal. Some of them could never forgive him; the boy educated to be a priest, but who had decided at the eleventh hour to follow another road, seemed to them a renegade, a vile traitor; and they hated and despised him accordingly. In fact the change was very small. He was fully convinced that the fullest use he could make of his life was to consecrate it to the quest of truth. He was born a priest, but what else is the true scientist?; he remained a lay priest—a priest of science—to the end of his days. His decision to leave the church affected his beliefs, changed his profession; but it did not alter the texture of his soul; it did not disturb his religion. Well might he say when he edited *The Future of Science* after a thoughtful interval of forty years, "My religion is still the progress of reason, that is, of science." And he added a little further in the same preface, "For us idealists, one single doctrine is true, the transcendent doctrine according to which the purpose of mankind is the creation of a superior conscience or, as they put it in the old days, the greatest glory of God."

8. HERBERT SPENCER

The life of a philosopher is generally less exciting than that of a war correspondent or a prima donna. Spencer's life is a very plain one indeed. If one does not insist on quoting the titles of the books and essays, which are the most conspicuous mile-stones of his career, it can be told in a few words. He was born in Derby on April 27, 1820, a thoroughbred Englishman. His father, George Spencer, was a teacher, a man of small means and little imagination, but honest to the core and of an unbending type. His mother, who does not seem to have influenced him to any extent, was very different from her husband, as patient and gentle as he was irritable and aggressively independent. They do not seem to have been very happy together, and their union was not blessed with many children who survived; although nine were born to them, only one, Herbert, the eldest, passed the stage of infancy. It is as if already the parents had been obliged to pay the heavy ransom of genius. The boy was left a great deal to himself, and he followed his bent toward scientific information, learning also a little English and arithmetic. At the age of thirteen, he was sent to his uncle, the Reverend Thomas Spencer, but the discipline of this new home seemed at first so hard to him that he ran away to his father's, walking one hundred and fifteen miles in three days with hardly any sleep or food. However, after a while he returned to his uncle and stayed with him, being tutored by him, chiefly in mathematics, for the next three years. This was the end of his systematic education, which certainly was very incomplete. When he began to earn his living at sixteen, he knew probably less than the average well-to-do boy of his age. It is true he knew considerably more in other ways, and he had also exercised to a greater extent his mother-wit. He worked successively as an assistant schoolmaster (for three months), as an engineer, and, after a vain attempt to earn a living as a literary man, he finally became in 1848 sub-editor of the *Economist*. This last position had the advantage of bringing him in touch with many eminent men of his day; men like Huxley, Tyndall, and Lewes. During all these years, he had carried on desultory reading, he had made quite a number of trivial inventions, he had done some writing and a considerable amount of solitary thinking.

The editing of the *Economist* left him time enough to complete his first book, *Social Statics*, which appeared early in 1851. In 1853, having inherited five hundred pounds from his uncle, he abandoned this position and determined to support himself by his own literary work. Such a decision is always hazardous; perhaps never more so than in the case of a man like Spencer who was less a writer than a thinker, whose ability to express himself was constantly inhibited by the fear of error. Shortly afterward, returning from a holiday in Switzerland, his health began to break down. Yet he resolutely pursued the self-imposed task of which he had become more and more conscious, and after many years of work and meditation, of suffering and disappointment, on March 27, 1860, he published the program of *A System of Philosophy*, the outline of the work to which the best part of his life was to be devoted. This is to me the culminating date in Spencer's life. It is then that he reveals for the first time his dominant personality.

Think of it! Here we have a man, whose systematic knowledge is rather small, whom many scientists (not the greatest, however) would have regarded as ignorant—and such he was in many respects—a man handicapped by lack of means and of health, but one who has been thinking hard and fast for a number of years, who has measured the world around him and himself, who knows exactly what he must do, who calmly estimates the immensity of the undertaking and the frailty of the means, who knows that his decision practically involves the surrender of his liberty for the rest of his days and makes of him a slave to his ideal—yet his faith is so great that he does not hesitate. No handicap will stop him and he sends his program to the world; a program to the fulfilment of which the rest of his life was faithfully and unrestrictedly given. One should keep in mind that at that time Spencer was already a nervous invalid; he could only work a few hours a day and had to use all sorts of tricks to do so without suffering; in the afternoon he had to forsake not simply work but any excitement or he would lose his night's rest. Yet he went ahead and henceforth his life was one of single-hearted devotion to his self-imposed trust. The first volume of the "Synthetic Philosophy" appeared in 1862, the tenth and last in 1896. It took him thirty-seven years.

It is not part of my present purpose to analyze, even briefly, Spencer's works. I will simply limit myself to a few remarks which may refresh the reader's memory and help him to appreciate Spencer's undertaking. Let us remember that his fundamental ideas are the following: First, an earnest belief in the value of philosophy as completely unified knowledge. Of course, without such belief, he could not have carried on his life's work. Secondly, the modern concept of evolution both in its biological and its universal import. Thirdly, the ideal of freedom—the core of his political thought.

I need not consider the first point because my whole essay is really devoted to it. It is remarkable that Spencer's first paper on evolution, one entitled "The Development Hypothesis," appeared as early as 1852, and his system of philosophy, which was essentially based upon the law of progress, was drafted by him for the first time in the early days of 1858. It is in the middle of the same year that Darwin and Wallace announced their theory of natural selection to the Linnæan Society of London. Spencer's merit as a precursor cannot be denied; at the same time it must be said that if his general theory of evolution was right, his conception of its mechanism was wrong. He believed that biologic progress was chiefly determined by the inheritance of characteristics gained by each individual during his lifetime, and although he later admitted the validity of Darwin's explanation, that is, natural selection, he nevertheless, remained a Lamarckian to the end of his life. Biologists are now generally agreed that acquired characters are *not* inherited, but their agreement on this subject is so recent that it would hardly be fair to blame Spencer on this score. Moreover, he was the first to extend this theory to a general conception of the universe and to retrace in the development not simply of living organisms, but of everything, an evolution or a progress "from the homogeneous to the heterogeneous, from the simple to the complex, from the incoherent to the coherent, from the indefinite to the definite." Matter-of-fact people may object that such a generalization is equally uncontrollable and useless, but that is to take a very crude view of the subject. Spencer's generalization, his insistence, was a powerful factor in the success of the evolutionary point of view. It helped mightily to create a new scientific and philosophic atmosphere. Is not that very much indeed, and what more could you expect a philosopher to do?

The "Synthetic Philosophy" did not embrace all the sciences. Feeling the necessity of restricting his field, chiefly on account of his insufficient scientific training, he made a systematic study only of those branches of knowledge to which the application of scientific methods was relatively new, to wit: biology, ethics, sociology. Biological facts had inspired his theory of evolution, and his biology in turn was dominated by it. On the other hand, in his ethical and social studies he was chiefly guided by the conception that liberty is the greatest good. The industrial and legal development of the last half-century seems to have proceeded in the opposite direction; yet the main difficulties of our moral and social life cannot be solved by artificial regulations, and now, even more than in Spencer's time, the greatest political problem to be solved is the one involved in the antinomy: freedom *versus* red tape, or initiative *versus* automatism, or life *versus* stagnation. Of course we all realize that a great many more regulations and social restrictions are needed than Spencer was prepared to admit, but the wise do not believe that these regulations are real factors of progress. The best that they can do is to prevent us from sliding backward; they cannot help us to go onward. They impede a certain amount of evil and they oblige another amount of it to assume a secret form, which may be on the whole less pernicious. They cannot create any parcel of positive good. Spencer's searching analysis of these subjects is of permanent value, and even if one assents to the temporary necessity of compulsory measures, there is no doubt that social progress lies mainly in the direction which he pointed out, the increase of *voluntary* co-operation.

Spencer has often been reproached that his system is based far more upon preconceived ideas than upon the observation of reality. Yet it must be admitted that he managed to marshal an enormous mass of facts to support his theories. If it be true that the latter were generally ahead of his experience, is not the same true to a certain extent of every scientific hypothesis? Never mind where a man gets his theories if he can establish them on experimental grounds. And Spencer, however biased and ignorant he may have been, took enormous pains to gather the experimental facts which he needed. Think only of the descriptive sociology whose publication began under his direction in 1873 and is not yet completed. Although he was very poor in the first half of his life and never reached more than a small competence, he spent more than three thousand pounds on this great undertaking. It is a pity, by the way, that the frame of these descriptions is so rigid and their size so awkward; but as they are, the published volumes contain an enormous amount of material and deserve greater recognition than they have ever received.

Spencer's main shortcoming was his dogmatism, his inability to consider the opinions of others. This dogmatism, which naturally increased as he grew older, arose partly from his initial ignorance, partly from his chronic neurasthenia, partly also from his lack of imagination, the singleness of his purpose, the exclusiveness of his thought. He was temperamentally a non-conformist, and although later in life he seemed to become more and more anxious to comply with the external conventions of society, I suppose he did so chiefly to eschew the criticism of fools and to protect his inner freedom.

There is no justification whatever for the statement that Spencer was "all brains and no heart." He was not sentimental, but very sensitive. Of course the accomplishment of his life's work did absorb the greatest part of his energy, including his emotional energy, and a man carrying such a burden on his shoulders could not be expected to run errands for others.

As in the case of Leonardo da Vinci, the predominance of his intellectual concerns partly explains his sexual indifference, which overwhelming interests of another sort could but aggravate, as he became more engrossed in his work. At any rate, Spencer does not seem to have ever experienced love. When he was twenty, he came nearer to it than ever before or afterward, but this little encounter seems very shadowy indeed and would not even be quoted in the biography of a more normal person. Later, while he was editing the *Economist,* he often took to the theater, to share his free tickets, a young girl (she was a year older than he) who then enjoyed some small notoriety for her translation of Strauss's *Life of Jesus.* They saw a great deal of one another, but although there is no woman for whom Spencer ever had a higher esteem, there is no warrant for the statement that they ever were in love. Leaving temperament aside, maybe if Spencer had had a little more imagination and pluck, they would have married. And just try to imagine what would have happened if Herbert Spencer and George Eliot had been man and wife! Pity that such experiments are impossible and that each life is definitive. Anyhow, I do not think, as far as I know them both, that Spencer would have made her happy; at least he could not have inspired her as deeply as did, later, George Henry Lewes.

It is very interesting to compare Spencer and Comte, and I love to bring them together in the field of my memory. Spencer did not like allusions to Comte apropos of himself, and he refused to own any indebtedness to his illustrious predecessor. It is true that he never made a formal study of Comte's works, yet he knew more of them than he himself was conscious of, as the result of his conversations with his friends, chiefly George Eliot and George Lewes, who were at one time enthusiastic followers of the French philosopher. They certainly had many opportunities of imparting to Spencer, willy-nilly, the gist of Comte's ideas.

However different the great Frenchman and the great Englishman were, they had very much in common. First of all their encyclopedic ideal, then their heroic faith and tenacity amidst untoward circumstances, their intolerance and dogmatism, their independence, their lack of those softening qualities which make men lovable. They attached a paramount importance to the study of sociology and positive polity, but they saw clearly that no real advance can be made which is not preceded by a moral transformation. They both asserted themselves in a similar way. Auguste Comte wrote the first sketch of his "Course of Positive Philosophy" in 1826, and the course itself was the labor of the next sixteen years; Spencer launched his manifesto in 1860, and working far more slowly, it took him more than double this time to produce the whole of his own synthesis.

Although both saw the importance of historical methods, they still have in common an extraordinary lack of historical sense. I am thinking of Comte, the philosopher—not of the prophet of his latter days, who, jumping to the other extreme, made of history a sort of religion. Before that, he does not seem to have grasped any more clearly than Spencer that genuine synthetic knowledge must comprehend the whole past of knowledge as well as its latest stages. Knowledge indeed is not something fixed and rigid, neither is it perfect; it is an ever-progressing organism whose meaning can only be understood by one who knows its origin and its inner life. Comte saw well enough that the history of intellectual development is the key to social evolution, but he did not see that it is also a master-key to synthetic knowledge. Spencer generously spent considerable sums for the elaboration of his "Descriptive Sociology," wherein the chronological sequence of events is faithfully abided by; yet what one might call his historical blindness was appalling. Nothing is more pitiful, nothing more calculated to make one doubt of his genius, than the meager notes he wrote while travelling in Egypt and Italy; to him the past was dead.

In my sketch of Spencer's life, I hope I have made it clear how ill prepared he was for the great undertaking upon which he had set his heart. At first view it seems unbelievable that he could do as much as he did with such inadequate equipment. In fact, he was not by any means as ignorant as one would expect such a poor student to be. If he had but few opportunities of systematic research or set studies, he had plenty, in his miscellaneous readings and his talks at the Athenæum or in the streets, with the most distinguished of his contemporaries, to gather in a substantial amount of first class information. His sharp and ready mind could make the most of the vaguest hint. Being endowed with a real genius for synthesis and possessing a complete system of knowledge, he could at the same time keep out all superfluous information, and let in, and classify at once, all that which was pertinent to his purpose.

In short, Spencer's mind was a genuine encyclopedic mind. The relative smallness of his knowledge was largely compensated by its congruity. The contemplation of such a mind helps one better than any explanation to understand what synthetic or encyclopedic knowledge actually is. It is not a mere accumulation of disconnected facts and theories. There are men who know thousands of facts, but have no skill in ordering them, no hooks in their brains to hang them on. The disintegrated knowledge of these men, of whom good people often speak as being very learned, is as remote from synthetic knowledge as crass ignorance. Knowledge is synthetic to the extent that it is unified, congruous, and the result of an organic growth. It cannot be obtained by mere juxtaposition of odd bits, but only by a slow digestion and re-elaboration of all the materials which the mind selects and absorbs.

Nevertheless, the lack of systematic training at the outset of his life was to Spencer a considerable and, to a large extent, an irretrievable handicap. Genius cannot entirely make up for the absence of the fundamental technique which can only be properly acquired when one is young. It is astounding that, barring such as were unavoidable at the time of his writing, there are not more errors in Spencer's philosophy, and that there is so much truth— truth of his day and prophetic truth—in a system resting on such a fragile foundation. Indeed the amount of active substance which his works contain is unusually great; an excellent proof of this is afforded by the extraordinary influence they exerted upon the intellectual development of the end of the nineteenth century.

The unification of knowledge is the more necessary as knowl- edge becomes more complex and specialized. If nobody had the courage to attempt it, the scientific world would soon become a new Tower of Babel. There are already too many specialists who know what they are doing hardly more than bees do. They work faithfully in their little corners, and their work is very useful. But science is far more than the sum of their fragmentary efforts. The growth of science is essentially an organic growth. That means that at least a few people must take the trouble to digest and assimilate the whole of it, in order to co-ordinate and to unify it. They may err; nay, they are bound to err ever and anon; but where one will err, the next one will go straight. It is so that every- thing progresses.

If encyclopedic efforts were abandoned, the amount of scien- tific facts and little theories might go on increasing indefinitely, but science would perish. The same is equally true of every human activity. Everywhere synthetic and centripetal endeavors must counterbalance the more special and centrifugal ones, lest the whole fabric of life be ruined and fall to pieces. Business men, for instance, have a very clear notion of this, and in proportion as they standardize and specialize their industries, they are careful to provide co-ordinating agencies to keep the complete body together.

But many will hasten to object: "Encyclopedic knowledge,

however desirable it may be, has become impossible. Science is becoming vaster every day and men do not seem to grow bigger. Indeed they seem smaller than they were in the past. There are no more Aristotles, and if one of these giants were to come back, the immensity of accumulated knowledge would make him feel like a pigmy. However narrow be the field one has chosen, one finds it impossible to encompass and to exhaust it. How then can it be possible to know the whole of science?" Their argument seems peremptory. Yet it is a fallacy based on the assumption that the whole of science is greater than any one of its parts. This is wrong, for when the parts and the whole are infinite, they are of equal size. It is just as difficult to know the history of France, or say the history of Paris, as the history of the world, because both undertakings are equally endless.

It is true that science is becoming more complex every day, but it is also becoming simpler and more harmonious in proportion as synthetic knowledge increases, that is, as more general relations are discovered. It is this very fact which makes encyclopedic efforts still possible. In some respects one might even say that such efforts are easier now than they were before, because the very progress of science enables one to contemplate its development from a higher point of view. The synthetic philosopher who has taken the pains to understand the most difficult parts of science and to climb, so to say, to its summit, enjoys the same advantage as a traveller who can view a whole country from the top of a mountain. No longer do the fantastically shaped hills, the crooked valleys, the deep and mysterious forests delude him; he sees them all from above in their correct relations. Of course he does not know every plant of every nook as does the plant-hunter, nor every insect as the zoologist, nor every stone of the rocks as the prospector. His knowledge is different. This suggests another reason for the possibility of encyclopedic knowledge. Such knowledge indeed is not necessarily vaster than any specialized knowledge, because he who undertakes to master it does not attempt to know, or at least to store in his memory, facts of the same kind. Many of the generalizations which the special investigator has reached at the cost of enormous pains are only elementary facts to the encyclopedist. It is easy enough for the map-maker to draw on his map a new river, to discover the true course of which many men have spent their lives; it is not more difficult for the encyclopedist to register new scientific facts and ideas, each of which is the fruit of considerable ingenuity and endless toil.

Yet most men prefer to stand on the solid ground of immediate experience. Their habits of work increase their timidity, and before long the most circumspect endeavors to organize empirical knowledge seems to them adventurous. It is perhaps chiefly as a contrast to this timidity that undertakings like Spencer's take heroic proportions.

There *is* a touch of heroism in them, because there is indeed a touch of adventure. Special research is generally less disappointing, for it brings immediate results and moral comfort. The astronomer who sets our clocks right and the chemist who prepares our dyes are just as conscious of their usefulness as the baker is; no doubts will prey on their minds. Again, to put neatly written cards in a drawer, or to classify endless rows of insects or shells, and then to write long memoirs in which every one of them is fastidiously described, will bring peace and happiness to many people. They well know that they are working for eternity, because it is they who bring together the materials of which any scientific synthesis is made. In the course of time many an edifice will be built with these materials; the buildings will pass, the materials will remain. Most scientists do not go beyond this; they prepare and collect material; they do not build. I suppose they obey a true instinct. They are quickly troubled with giddiness. They are right in refusing to go farther; they are wrong when they say that everybody is dizzy when they are.

The proof that synthetic studies are not necessarily more difficult than others, for one who has the proper constitution, is that Spencer, whose systematic training was so poor and who could not work more than two or three hours a day, succeeded so well. He succeeded because of the synthetic power of his mind, but also because of his indomitable will, of his tenacity, of his faith.

And Spencer's relative success gives one much hope, for it is easy to conceive of a man having his synthetic grasp, his faith, and far more systematic knowledge and physical endurance. One has only to think of a Spencer endowed with a greater reserve of health and a competence which would have enabled him in his youth to pursue long university studies and to master the rudiments and the technique of many sciences. One may object that Spencer's audacity was partly the result of his ignorance. That is plausible. Ignorance has been more than once a source of inspiration; on the other hand, knowledge is always a heavy burden to bear. Many are so overburdened that they can hardly move. But again we may conceive a man strong enough to accumulate a great deal of experience, and yet to remain imaginative and young and keep a clear vision of his purpose.

Let us think of Spencer with gratefulness, not so much for the knowledge which he added to ours, as for the example of moral courage and of faith which he gave us. He helped us to understand the nature and the desirability of synthetic science, to realize its possibility and to keep alive the need and the love of it. As long as there are men who care not simply for material results, but yearn for unified and harmonious knowledge, the memory of Herbert Spencer will be revered.

PART THREE

EAST AND WEST

9. EAST AND WEST IN THE HISTORY OF SCIENCE

When one speaks of the history of science most people think of experimental and mathematical knowledge as we know it now, with its inexhaustible harvest of applications; they think of what we would call "modern science," the development of which was hardly started before the seventeenth century. This is of course justifiable in some respects, yet he who was acquainted only with that part of the story would have a very misleading idea of the whole evolution. It is as if he knew a man only in his maturity and was not aware that such maturity was made possible only by the long years of childhood and adolescence.

The comparison of mankind with a single man helps us to understand both. Let us make use of it. What would you think of a biography which began, let us say, at a time when the hero was thirty, was married and already had children, and was well started on his work? Would not such a biography be very disappointing? For we would want to know how he got started, whom he had married, how he became interested in his chosen work and gradually devoted all of his thought and energy to it. For exactly the same reasons a history of science beginning only in the sixteenth or seventeenth century is not only incomplete but fundamentally wrong. This is even more true in the case of mankind than in that of a single man, because in the latter case we can at least imagine various possibilities. If we have read many biographies of men of science we have in our minds a sort of composite picture of their youth which may serve as a first approximation. But in the case of mankind it is simply impossible to imagine the history of the four or five millennia of recorded experience which preceded the advent of modern science.

It is unfortunately true that many scientists lack a cultural background, and because of this do not like to look backward. It is a vicious circle: why should they look that way if there is nothing for them to see? Their history of science does not even go as far back as the seventeenth century; they are prone to believe that almost everything worthwhile was done in the nineteenth or in the twentieth century. Now in this they are most certainly wrong. The most astounding results were obtained in the most recent times, simply because they were the latest; but these results were made possible only by all antecedent efforts; they would have been utterly impossible without them. All the preparatory work left undone by our ancestors would have to be done by us now or by our children later. The results of the present are more complex, and more valuable than those of the past, in fact they have superseded the latter; but there is every reason to suppose that in their turn they will be superseded by those of the future. At all times there have been "moderns" who could not help thinking that their ways as compared with those of the "ancients" were almost final. One of the main functions of the history of science is to correct such mistakes and to give us, who are the "moderns" of today, a less conceited view of our share in the total of human evolution. Of course this age of ours is a very wonderful one, and, for us who are living in it, is undoubtedly for that very reason the most wonderful of all; but we must bear in mind that such privileged ages have succeeded one another as the generations themselves. Even as young lovers have sincerely felt in their exaltation that the world was never more beautiful than as they saw it, even so each great discovery which enabled scientists to penetrate somewhat deeper below appearances and to push the barriers of ignorance and darkness a little further away, may have given them the illusion that they had finally reached the heart of the mystery and that they were the first to understand the universe thoroughly.

There is also a very good practical and philosophical motive for devoting at least as much attention to the more distant achievements as to the later ones, and that is, that the former, although so much easier to explain, give us a far better conception of the meaning of scientific evolution. To begin with, they are spread over a much longer period. Modern science, as defined above, is after all hardly more than three centuries old, while the previous evolution was a matter of more than four millennia, that is, without counting the innumerable centuries of which we have no definite records. The development of ancient and medieval science is not only a much longer stretch, but if I may put it so, a collection of stretches of various lengths interrupted and bent by all kinds of vicissitudes. When we consider the whole of it, we can verify the fact that human evolution is infinitely more complex than the very orderly progress of the last centuries would indicate. Scientific research is now organized with such elaboration and in so many countries that a long and complete interruption of it is hardly conceivable, and we almost expect discoveries to follow each other without cease and without end. In the distant past, on the contrary, there was so much discontinuity and hesitation in scientific progress, that the latter seemed to be even more fortuitous than it really was. A discovery was like a gold nugget one might stumble upon or not according to one's luck. By way of contrast much of the scientific work of to-day might be compared to the systematic exploitation of a gold mine, the average output of which can be foretold.

That comparison is a little exaggerated on both sides, but the fact remains that scientific progress was far more erratic in the past than it is now, and that considerably more energy was wasted in vain efforts and along hopeless paths. As a result, a vision of medieval man groping for the truth is somewhat bewildering: he seems to be going in too many directions at once and to be turning in circles. There is a general direction, however, but to perceive it one must look from a great distance and be able to disregard all the irrelevant movements, all the stops, lapses, detours and retrogressions. We are now sufficiently distant from ancient or even medieval science to appreciate the meaning of almost every step of it, true or false. On the contrary, we cannot yet see the latest developments of science in their true perspective. Of course, we believe we can; we think in good faith that we can single out the most pregnant discoveries of our own days, but the whole of past history is there to testify that contemporary judgments are always precarious. This is natural enough. The value of a theory, the importance of a fact, depend entirely on the conclusions which may be derived from them, on the fruits they will bear, and scientists are not prophets. Comte's saying, "Savoir afin de prévoir," is often misquoted. It is true the scientist is able to foresee and to anticipate the immediate consequences of certain events, and therein lies the secret of his material power. But he is not able to predict the future except within the very narrow sector controlled by his knowledge and even there he is hedged in with all kinds of restrictions. Indeed no man is more chary of predictions than the true scientist.

There are two main reasons for studying the history of science: a purely historical one, to analyze the development of civilization, i.e., to understand man, and a philosophical one, to understand the deeper meaning of science. Now from either point of view, the history of ancient and medieval science is at least as useful as that of modern science. He who knows only one of these histories does not really know the history of science, nor does he know the history of civilization.

I shall try to make this more concrete by dealing at greater length with the earlier parts of our history. If it were not so futile to pick out a single period as the best—for each period was the best from a certain point of view and each was an indispensable link in the chain of ages—I would say in opposition to the uncritical scientist that the most important was, not the latest, but the earliest. Nothing is more difficult than to begin. And what can be more fundamental than a good beginning? Is it not the foundation upon which all the rest will be built?

Unfortunately we shall never have any adequate information on this, the most critical period of man's history, when he was gratifying his urgent needs and slowly emerging out of the darkness, when his instinctive craving for power and for knowledge was beginning to appear. Who first thought of kindling a fire? Who invented the earliest stone implements? Who domesticated the animals which have shared our lives ever since? How did language develop? And later, much later, writing? Who conceived the wheel? Just think of these discoveries and of their infinite implications. Without articulate language man remained an animal. Without writing, the safe transmission and preservation of knowledge were impossible. Progress implies safe keeping of what we already have. Without writing, the accumulation of knowledge was precarious and limited, progress small and uncertain. Can any one of our modern discoveries, however startling, begin to compare with those which made possible all the others? And yet we know nothing about them. We can hardly guess. It is probable that they involved the secular collaboration of thousands of men, each big step forward being finally secured by the exceptional genius of some of them. The evolutions leading to each of these fundamental discoveries were exceedingly slow—almost comparable to the biologic transitions from one type to another—so slow that the people who took part in them were utterly unaware of them. Genius was then required only from time to time to clinch the results obtained by the unconscious accumulation of infinitesimal efforts, to secure what was gained and prepare another slow movement in the same general direction.

The total evolution which prepared the dawn of science must have taken tens of thousands of years. By the beginning of the third millennium before Christ it was already completed in at least two countries: Mesopotamia and Egypt, and possibly in two others, India and China. The people of Mesopotamia and Egypt had then already attained a high stage of culture including the use of writing, and a fair amount of mathematical, astronomical and medical knowledge. Thus it would seem proved that civilization began in the East. *Ex oriente lux, ex occidente lex.* From the East came the light, from the West, law! This aphorism contains a good deal of truth and might be chosen as the motto of my essay.

Let me say right away that my aim is to show the immense contributions which Eastern people made to our civilization, even if our idea of civilization is focused upon science. We are used to thinking of our civilization as western, we continually oppose our western ways to the eastern ways, and we have sometimes the impression that the opposition is irreducible.

"Oh, East is East, and West is West, and never the twain shall meet."

Now that impression is false, and as it is likely to do considerable mischief in both East and West, it is worthwhile to disclose the error as fully as possible. However divided it may be with regard to material interests and other trifles, mankind is essentially united with regard to its main purpose. East and West are often opposed one to the other, but not necessarily so, and it is wiser to consider them as two visages, or let us say, as two moods of the same man.

Ex oriente lux! There is no doubt whatever that our earliest scientific knowledge is of oriental origin. As to the possible Chinese and Hindu origins we cannot say much that is definite, but, on the contrary, with regard to Mesopotamia and Egypt we are on very solid ground.

For example, as early as the middle of the fourth millennium before Christ the Egyptians were already acquainted with a decimal system of numbers. In an inscription of that time there is reference to 120,000 captives, 400,000 oxen, and 1,422,000 goats, each decimal unit being represented by a special symbol. By the middle of the following millennium Sumerians had developed a highly technical system of accounting. The astronomical knowledge of these people was equally remarkable. The Egyptian calendar of 365 days was established in 4241 B.C. Babylonians accumulated planetary observations for astrological purposes: e.g., elaborate observations of Venus go back to the twentieth century B.C. They compiled lists of stars and were soon able to predict eclipses.

That early knowledge was not only abundant, but highly systematized. In the case of Egypt we are especially well informed because we have two early papyri, each of which might be called a treatise. The earliest, the Golenishchev papyrus of Moscow, dates from the middle of the nineteenth century B.C. but is copied from an older document of the end of the third millennium; the second, the Rhind papyrus, kept in London and New York, dates from the middle of the seventeenth century B.C. but is a copy of a text which may be at least two centuries older. The second of these texts has been studied with extreme care by a number of investigators. The latest edition of it by Arnold Buffum Chace, chancellor of Brown University, Ludlow Bull, H. P. Manning, and R. C. Archibald (1927-29) is at once so complete and so attractive that I am sure it will turn the hearts of many men and women to the study of Egyptian antiquities. I imagine that the first re-action of some people, if they were shown these sumptuous volumes, would be one of wonder that so much time and money should have been spent on an early text of so little scientific value from the point of view of our present knowledge, but I am sure that it would not take long to convert them to an entirely different attitude. For just think what it means. Here we have a mathe-matical treatise which was written more than thirteen centuries before the time of Euclid! To be sure it does not compare with the latter's *Elements*, and we are not surprised that more than a millennium of additional efforts were needed to build up the latter, but it contains already such elaborate results that we must consider it, not as a beginning, but rather as a climax, the climax of a very long evolution. The Egyptian mathematicians of the seventeenth century were already able to solve complicated prob-lems involving determinate and indeterminate equations of the first degree and even of the second; their arithmetical ingenuity was astounding; they used the method of false position and the rule of three; they could find the area of a circle and of a sphere with a very remarkable approximation; they could measure the volume of a cylinder and of the frustum of a square pyramid. But is it necessary to insist upon their mathematical accomplishments?

Pyramids? Did I mention pyramids? Do not these gigantic witnesses of the Egyptian genius speak loudly enough? The great pyramid of Gizeh dates from the beginning of the thirtieth century B.C. In our age of mechanical wonders, its mass is still as imposing as when it was built almost five thousand years ago; it seems as permanent as the hills and in all probability will outlast most of the skyscrapers of which we are so proud. However startling our first vision of it, our admiration increases as we analyze the achievement and measure the amount of mathematical and engineering skill, of experience and discipline, which were needed to bring it to a successful conclusion. No wonder that so many scholars lost their wits for pondering too much on the subject!

If we pass to medicine, other surprises are in store for us. The Greek god of healing, Asclepius, was but a descendant of the Egyptian one, Imhotep, and the history of the latter can be traced back to a real personality, that of a learned physician who flourished probably at the beginning of the thirtieth century B.C. What does this mean again? We often speak of Hippocrates, and we like to call him the Father of Medicine; we shall better appreciate Imhotep's antiquity when we realize that Hippocrates is more than halfway between him and us. The chances are that Imhotep's medical knowledge was but rudimentary, but it cannot have been insignificant—otherwise his apotheosis would hardly have occurred. However this was only a beginning, or more correctly, a new beginning. Let some thirteen centuries elapse, and we reach the golden age of Egyptian science—the age to which the Rhind papyrus belongs. Strangely enough we have also a medical treatise of the same age, the Edwin Smith papyrus, of which Professor Breasted has prepared an edition. This is not like other papyri, a collection of recipes and charms, but a systematic treatise arranged *"a capite ad calcem"*—from head to foot—an order which was followed down to the end of our Middle Ages. It contains the consideration of forty-eight cases, each of which is reported in the same order: name, examination, diagnosis, judgment, treatment, gloss.

These examples will convince you that a considerable body of systematized knowledge was far anterior to Greek science. In fact this helps to explain what one might call the miracle of Greek civilization. To be sure no intelligent man could read the *Iliad* and the *Odyssey*, which were the primitiae of that civilization, without wondering what had made such masterpieces possible. They could not possibly appear like bolts from the blue. Like every glorious beginning, this was not only the prelude of one evolution but the end, the climax, of another. Students of Greek mathematics, of Greek astronomy, and Greek medicine could not help asking themselves similar questions. How could the relative perfection of the Greek scientific treatises be accounted for? The explanation is still very incomplete, but no doubt exists as to the main fact: the Greeks borrowed a large quantity of observations and of crude theories from the Egyptians and the peoples of Mesopotamia. Unfortunately, it is hardly possible in any case to describe the complete transmission of elements from, say, Egypt to Hellas. This is partly due to the revolutionary events which occurred about the beginning of the first millennium; these events were probably connected with the early use of iron (instead of bronze) and almost obliterated the older Aegean culture. Our ignorance may be dissipated by later archaeological discoveries, for example by the deciphering of Minoan and Mycenaean texts, but it is doubtful whether the whole story will ever be revealed to us, for the introduction of the iron age was an upheaval of extraordinary magnitude and destructiveness. At any rate, in the present state of our knowledge, there is a gap of more than a thousand years between the golden age of Egyptian science and the golden age of Greek science. We are certain that much of the

Greek knowledge was borrowed from eastern sources but we do not know exactly when or how the borrowings took place.

For example, the incubation rites which were practiced in the Greek Asclepieia were in all probability derived from Egyptian models. These rites were very important from our point of view because, thanks to them, a large number of clinical observations were concentrated in the temples, especially in the most famous ones, Epidauros and Pergamon, Cos and Cnidos. The value of such concentration requires no emphasis, least of all for the medical art; for to make scientific inductions, it is not enough to have observations, one must have plenty of them. Without some means of collecting abundant clinical cases such as were afforded by the Asclepieia, the progress of medicine would have been considerably slower. It is not too much to say that the Asclepieia were the cradles of Greek medicine, and they help to account for the extraordinary richness of the Hippocratic collection—but we must not forget that they themselves inherited and continued Egyptian traditions.

On the other hand, Greek astronomy was largely of Babylonian origin, though it was also inspired by Egyptian examples. The Babylonian influence continued to make itself felt throughout historic times, and it is probable that the precession of the equinoxes was first discovered not by Hipparchos but by the Babylonian astrologer Kidinnu (c. 343 b.c.); whether Hipparchos borrowed that discovery from Kidinnu or not, it is certain that he could not have made it without reference to the ancient Babylonian observations. With regard to arithmetic, the continuation of Babylonian and Egyptian influences is very striking. The Greek preference for expressing ordinary fractions as the sum of fractions with numerator unity and their use of a special symbol for 2/3 were obviously Egyptian relics, while their sexagesimal fractions were Babylonian.

There is perhaps no more fascinating subject than the study of the transition from oriental science to the early Greek, and the archaeological investigations which are being feverishly con-

ducted by scholars of many nationalities all over the Near East
are keeping it in a state of flux which is in itself a stimulus. It is
perhaps wiser not to indulge in predictions with regard to such a
live subject; yet it is safe to say that, however numerous the
Greek borrowings may prove to have been, the blossoming of the
Greek scientific genius remains almost equally difficult to account
for. Students of art and literature are confronted with a similar
difficulty, and when we speak of the "Greek miracle" we do nothing but confess to it and admit our ignorance. In fact the difficulty and the miracle are even greater in the case of science than
in that of art, for there are Egyptian statues of the early dynasties
which are not a whit inferior to the best Greek productions, while
the Egyptian scientific treatises, however remarkable, especially
when their high antiquity is considered, do not begin to compare
with their Greek offspring. Between the scribe Aḥmôse (the
writer of the Rhind papyrus) and, say, Hippocrates of Chios,
there is such a gigantic difference that some critics have gone so
far as to deny the scientific nature of the Egyptian work altogether
and to consider it only as a collection of empirical recipes. In this
they were certainly mistaken, for the Egyptian knowledge was far
from being fragmentary and accidental; it was already methodical
to a degree, and hence scientific. Yet the doubts of these critics
are somewhat justified by the immensity of the gap. We do not
know what happened between the seventeenth and the sixth centuries B.C., and it would be rash to conclude that the Egyptian
knowledge was not gradually improved; however the chances are
that the main improvements were made not by Egyptians, nor by
Minoans or Mycenaeans (whoever these were), but by Greeks,
the favored people whose earliest "Book" and witness was the
Iliad. And these improvements were of such magnitude that they
raised science to a higher level. When a student of ancient science
grows a little rhapsodical about it, we may be tempted to ascribe
his enthusiasm to the one-sidedness and the consequent blindness
of his devotion. But I have devoted far more time and thought to
the science of the Middle Ages than to that of Antiquity, and my

admiration for the latter has not ceased to increase as I knew the former better.

The spirit of Greek science, which accomplished such wonders within a period of about five centuries, was essentially the western spirit, whose triumphs are the boast of modern scientists. But we must bear in mind two important qualifications. First, that the foundations of that Greek science were wholly oriental, and, however deep the Greek genius, it is not certain that it could have built anything comparable to its actual achievements without those foundations. When discussing the fate of a man of genius we may make many suppositions, but it would be absurd to wonder what would have happened if he had had other parents, for then he would never have been. In the same way we have no right to disregard the Egyptian father and the Mesopotamian mother of the Greek genius. In the second place, while that genius was creating what might be called (in opposition to Egyptian science on one hand and to medieval science on the other) the beginning of modern science, another development, equally miraculous, but of an entirely different kind, was taking place in an oriental country near the easternmost end of the Mediterranean Sea. While Greek philosophers were trying to give a rational explanation of the world and boldly postulated its physical unity, the Hebrew prophets were establishing the moral unity of mankind upon the notion of a single God. These two developments were not parallel but complementary; they were equally momentous but entirely independent; in spite of their spatial proximity they proceeded for centuries in almost complete ignorance of one another. They did not really come together until the end of ancient times, and their union was finally cemented upon the prostrate bodies of the two civilizations which gave birth to them.

I shall come back to that presently. But I must first explain the decadence and fall of the Greek spirit. After having made so many conquests in such magnificent style, why did it stop? One cannot help feeling that if that spirit had kept its valor for a few

more centuries, human progress would have been considerably
accelerated and the course of civilization would have been very
different. What befell it? It is impossible to answer such a question; one can only guess, and even our guesses are necessarily
very timid. What would we answer in the case of a single man if
his best work was done when he was twenty, and the rest of his
life spent in sterile idleness? We would say simply: His genius
failed him. That would not be a complete explanation, but it
would satisfy us. But can such an explanation hold for a whole
nation? Why not? If we speak of the Greek genius at all, as a sort
of natural integration, we may conceive the possibility of its
gradual corruption and disappearance. If it could emerge, why
could it not be submerged again and fail altogether?

What happened to Greece is that the intellectual activities of
its people were hopelessly out of proportion to their political
wisdom and their morality. A house divided against itself must
necessarily fall, a body rent by internal strife is foredoomed to
destruction, above all such a body is soon incapable of any kind
of creation.* It was not simply Greek science that disappeared,
but Greek art and literature as well. One might speculate as to
what would have happened if the Greek and Hebrew ideals had
been nursed together instead of separately, or at any rate, if they
had not grown for so long in complete isolation. Such speculations
are vain of course, and yet they force themselves upon us. The
fact is, the Greek and the Hebrew spirits were incompatible; they
could not have grown together and corrected one another; rather
they would have destroyed each other. After all, it was perhaps
necessary that each be built as solidly as possible on its own basis.
It is likely that any premature synthesis would have stunted the
development of both. When studying the records of the past, one

---

* The following quotation from Euripides is typical, for it betrays political indifference as
well as scientific interest. The Greeks carried their political sluggishness and immorality
so far that they ceased to exist as a nation, and jeopardized not only their political but also
their intellectual life. "Blessed is he who has attained scientific knowledge, who seeks
neither the troubles of citizenship nor rushes into unjust deeds, but contemplates the ageless
order of immortal nature, how it is constituted and when and why. . . ."

has often the impression that men can grasp but one idea at a time.

The reader knows how Greece was finally conquered by Rome, and how in the course of time it conquered its conquerors. Yet the old spirit was subdued, and Roman science even at its best was always but a pale imitation of the Greek. The Romans were so afraid of disinterested research, the excess of which had been one of the causes of the Greek corruption, that they went to the other extreme and discouraged any research the utilitarian value of which was not immediately obvious.

In the meanwhile, Jesus Christ had appeared and told the world a new message, a message of love and humility, universal in its scope: Charity does not need knowledge; blessed are the pure in spirit, the pure in heart; on the other hand, knowledge without charity is not only useless but pernicious; it can but lead to pride and damnation. The development of Christianity was a first attempt to bring together the Hebrew and the Greek spirits, but as the Roman Christians hardly understood the former and misunderstood the latter thoroughly, the attempt was an utter failure.

A good example of those misunderstandings may be found in the work of Tatian, a Syrian convert who lived in Galen's time. His Greek oration "against the Greeks" contains not only an account of the weaknesses of paganism but the most extravagant claims in behalf of oriental peoples. According to him the Greeks had invented nothing; they had borrowed all their knowledge from others—Assyrians, Phoenicians, Egyptians; their only superiority was in the art of writing and of lying. Thus after centuries of ignorance of Eastern achievements, some Eastern Greeks, whose minds were poisoned against Greek civilization by Christian prejudices, were going to the other extreme. Apparently Greeks and Orientals were not fated to understand one another.

We may say that the Greek spirit, that disinterested love of truth which is the very spring of knowledge, was finally smothered by the combination of Roman utilitarianism and Christian sentimentality. Again let us dream for a moment, and wonder what might have happened if the Greeks and the Christians had seen their respective good points instead of seeing only the evil ones. How beautiful if their two types of other-worldliness could have been harmonized! How many miseries mankind would have been spared! But it was not to be. The path of progress is not straight but very crooked; the general direction is clear enough, but only if one considers a very long stretch of it from far off. Before being able to reconcile the love of truth with the love of man, the scientific spirit with the Golden Rule, mankind was obliged to make many strange and cruel experiments.

To begin with, under the influence of Christian education combined with Roman narrow-mindedness and later with Barbarian ignorance, the connection with Greek culture—which was the only source of positive knowledge—became looser and looser. The debasement of thought is well illustrated by the fact that even in the Byzantine empire, where there was no linguistic barrier to the transmission of ancient science, much of the latter remained practically unknown. This is so true that in the thirteenth and fourteenth centuries, when the Latin world was finally awakened, Byzantine scholars preparing a scientific revival retranslated from the Arabic and the Latin a number of writings which were nothing but translations from the Greek or poor imitations of such translations. Their intellectual indigence was such that they did not recognize the work of their own ancestors.

The contact between ancient Greece and western Christendom ended by being so precarious that it might have conceivably been broken altogether, but for the intervention of another oriental people, the Arabs. Please note that this was the third great wave of oriental wisdom, the third time that the creative impulse came from the East. The first initiative—and the most fundamental of all—came from Egypt and Mesopotamia; the second from Israel, and though it influenced science only in an indirect way, it was also of incalculable pregnancy; the third, with which I am going to deal now, came from Arabia and from Persia.

About the year A.D. 610, a new prophet appeared at Mecca, in Hejaz, Abû-l-Qâsim Muhammad of the tribe of Quraysh, who was like a new incarnation of the old Hebrew prophets. At first the people did not pay much attention to him, but after he had abandoned his native town and moved two hundred and fifty-five miles northward to al-Medina, in 622, his success was phenomenal. No prophet was ever more successful. By the time of his death ten years later, he had managed to unite the Arabian tribes and to inspire them with a single-hearted fervor which would enable them later to conquer the world. Damascus was captured in 635, Jerusalem in 637; the conquest of Egypt was completed in 641, that of Persia in the following year, that of Spain somewhat later in 710/12. By this time the Muslims, that is the Prophet's followers, were ruling a large belt of the world all the way from Central Asia to the Far West. The conquest of Persia was especially momentous because it brought the invaders, brave but uncouth, into touch with an old and very refined civilization, that of Iran. I did not speak of it before because it is difficult to state its earlier contributions with sufficient brevity, and more difficult, if not impossible, to date them. For the purpose of a sketch like this, it is sufficient to introduce Iran at this juncture, but its part henceforth was considerable. The new dynasty of Muslim caliphs, the 'Abbâsid (750-1258) established its capital in Baghdâd on the Tigris, and for a time that new city was one of the main centers of the civilized world. The 'Abbâsids were from the beginning under the Iranian spell. Their religious and moral strength was derived from their ancestral home, Arabia; their urbanity, their humanism, from Persia. To put it in a nutshell, the new Muslim civilization was essentially due to the grafting of the vigorous Arabic scion upon the old Iranian tree. This explains at once its astounding robustness and its changing qualities.

Under the impulse of these two tremendous forces, Muslim fanaticism and Persian curiosity, and under the guidance of a series of 'Abbâsid caliphs who had a passion for knowledge—

al-Manṣūr, Hārūn al-Rashīd, al-Ma'mūn—the new civilization developed with incredible speed and efficacy. It was doubly rooted in the past: the Prophet had transmitted to them with very few modifications Semitic monotheism and morality, and their Persian tutors had incited them to drink deeply from the older sources of learning, Sanskrit and Greek. From the Hindus they learned arithmetic, algebra, trigonometry, iatrochemistry; from the Greeks, logic, geometry, astronomy, and medicine. It did not take them long to realize the immensity of the Greek treasure and they had no rest until the whole of it (that is, as much as was available to them) was translated into Arabic.

In this enterprise they received invaluable help from the Syrians and other Christian subjects of the Caliphate who spoke Greek, Syriac, and pretty soon Arabic. These Oriental Christians, though somewhat Hellenized, had always been treated with suspicion and disfavor by the Byzantine government, and if (as is very probable) they shared Tatian's views, it is not surprising that no love was lost between them. Being repulsed and persecuted by the Greeks, their readiness to help their Muslim conquerors was not astonishing. The Syrians spoke Arabic with so much alacrity that they gradually allowed this new language to supersede their own. These born polyglots were natural intermediaries; it is they who prepared the earliest translations from the Greek into Arabic and who initiated their masters in the Greek knowledge. Thus were the first bridges between Hellas and Islām built by Christians.

The immense cultural importance of Islām lies in the fact that it finally brought together the two great intellectual streams which had flowed independently in ancient times. Previous attempts, as I have already indicated, had failed. Jews and Greeks had mixed in Alexandria but, in spite of the fact that the former had learned the language of the latter and that one of their learned men, Philo, had made a deep study of both traditions, there had been no real fusion. The Christians had not succeeded any better, because of their single-hearted devotion to the new Gospel, which reduced

everything else to futility in their eyes. Now, for the first time in
the history of the world, Semitic religion and Greek knowledge
actually combined in the minds of many people. Nor was that
integration restricted to a single city or country; the new culture
spread like a prairie fire from Baghdād eastward to India, Trans-
oxiana and further still, and westward to the very edge of the
world.

Muslim culture was at once deeply unified and very diversified.
The peoples of Islām were kept together and separated from the
rest of the world by the two strongest bonds which can bind a
human community, religion and language. One of the few duties
of a learned Muslim is the reading of the Qur'ān (their Bible),
and it must be read in Arabic. Thanks to this religious obligation,
Arabic, which before Muḥammad had no more than a tribal
importance, became a world language. After the eleventh century
it lost its hegemony, but remained very important; it is still one
of the languages most widely used at the present time. It has
gradually been split into a number of dialectal forms, even as
Latin disintegrated into the various Romance languages; but
with these radical distinctions that, up to this day, every literate
Muslim must have some knowledge of classical Arabic to read the
Qur'ān, and that the written language—e.g., that used in the news-
papers—continues to approximate more or less the classical standards. While each Romance language has its own written form, its
own standards of perfection, one may say that there is for the
Arabic writer all over the world but one model of excellence,
that given by the Qur'ān and by the best authors of the classical
age. Because of their single language and of their common faith,*
ideas traveled with astounding regularity and speed from one end
of the Dār al-Islām to the other.

The universal extension of that culture caused necessarily many

---

* To be sure, Islām was soon divided into a number of sects and schools, and one finds in
it the same gamut of religious forms as in Christianity—from the extreme fundamentalism
and the strangest mystical aberrations at the right to the purist unitarianism at the left; yet,
however different, these were all forms of the same Muslim faith. Every Muslim read the
same Scriptures.

diversities. Muslims were brought closely into touch with all kinds
of unbelievers—in the East, Chinese, Mongols, Malays, Hindus;
further West, Magians, Syrians, Greeks, Copts; further still,
Berbers in Africa; Sicilians, Spaniards, and other Franks in southern Europe; Jews everywhere. These contacts were generally
friendly, or at least not unfriendly, for the Muslims treated their
ra'āyā (subjects) with kind and tolerant condescension. Under
their patronage, many important works were published in Arabic
by non-Muslims: Sabians, Christians, Jews, Samaritans. The
great chemist, Jābir ibn Ḥaiyān, was probably a Sabian; al-Battānī
was certainly of Sabian origin but had embraced Islām; the
physicians Ḥunain ibn Isḥāq, Ibn Buṭlān and Ibn Jazla were
Christians. Down to the twelfth century Arabic was the philosophic and scientific language of the Jews; for example, the
famous *Guide of the Perplexed*, the greatest Jewish treatise of
the Middle Ages, was written by Maimonides in Arabic. What is
more, the earliest Hebrew grammars were composed also in
Arabic, not in Hebrew. In other words the medieval Jews were so
deeply Arabicized, that they needed Arabic assistance for the
scientific study of their own sacred language.*

During the first two centuries of the Hegira the whole of Islām
was ruled by the Ummayad and 'Abbāsid caliphs, but after that
the caliphate was gradually broken into an increasing number of
independent kingdoms of all kinds and sizes. The political dis-
integration caused intense rivalries, intellectual ones as well as
others, between the different Muslim courts. Instead of one or
two centers of culture, like Baghdād and Cordova, there grew up
little by little a whole series of them: Ghazna, Samarqand, Marv,
Herât, Ṭūs, Nīshāpūr, Ray, Isfahān, Shīrāz, Mūṣul, Damascus,
Jerusalem, Cairo, Qairawān, Fās, Marrākush, Toledo, Seville,
Granada, etc., etc. The obligation for every Muslim to perform,
if possible, the Pilgrimage to Mecca brought about incessant com-
munications between the different parts of Islām and originated

---

* In a similar way, American Jews study Hebrew grammar in English books, but the
analogy ends here. Hebrew grammar was actually born in an Arabic cradle.

numberless personal meetings between scholars hailing from the more distant countries. Under that influence many learned Muslims seemed to be affected with a kind of *Wanderlust*, for it was not unusual for them to perform the Pilgrimage more than once, making considerable stops in the main cities on their way, renewing contacts with their colleagues, engaging in long discussions, copying manuscripts, or composing their own writings; this one in Andalusia, another in the Maghrib, another in Egypt, and so forth. Thus (and also because of the common language) scientific knowledge obtained in any part of Islām was transmitted with astounding celerity to the others, and fresh stimulations were constantly exchanged.

The almost unbelievable vigor of the new culture may be well measured by the international triumph of the Arabic language, a triumph which was the more remarkable because that language was not ready for the occasion but had to be elaborated as the need for it increased, and became more and more technical. The Qur'ānic idiom was very beautiful indeed but limited. As the immense task of pouring out the Greek treasure into the Arabic vessels proceeded, it was necessary to make new vessels and better ones. Not only that, but a great majority of the people who used them had to begin by learning how from the very rudiments. And yet within a couple of centuries multitudes had acquired some familiarity with that language which had been utterly unknown to their ancestors, if not to their parents.

The briefest enumeration of the Arabic contributions to knowledge would be too long to be inserted here, but I must insist on the fact that, though a major part of the activity of Arabic-writing scholars consisted in the translation of Greek works and their assimilation, they did far more than that. They did not simply transmit ancient knowledge, they created a new one. To be sure, none of them attained the highest peaks of the Greek genius. No Arabic mathematician can begin to compare with Archimedes or Apollonius. Ibn Sīnā makes one think of Galen, but no Arabic physician had the wisdom of Hippocrates. However, such comparisons are hardly fair, for a few Greeks had reached, almost suddenly, extraordinary heights. That is what we call the Greek miracle. But one might speak also, though in a different sense, of an Arabic miracle. The creation of a new civilization of international and encyclopedic magnitude within less than two centuries is something that we can describe, but not completely explain. This movement, as opposed to the Greek, was perhaps more remarkable for its quantity than for its quality. Yet it was creative; it was the most creative movement of the Middle Ages down to the thirteenth century. The Arabic-writing scientists elaborated algebra (the name is telltale) and trigonometry on Greco-Hindu foundations; they reconstructed and developed— though, it must be said, very little—Greek geometry; they collected abundant astronomical observations and their criticisms of the Ptolemaic system, though not always justified, helped to prepare the astronomical reformation of the sixteenth century; they enriched enormously our medical experience; they were the distant originators of modern chemistry; they improved the knowledge of optics, and meteorology, the measurement of densities; their geographical investigations extended from one end of the world to the other; they published a number of annals of capital interest, dealing with almost every civilized country outside of western Christendom; one of their historians, the Berber Ibn Khaldūn, expounded a philosophy of history which was by far the most elaborate and the most original of medieval times; finally they laid down the principles of Semitic philology.

Surely these were no mean achievements. If they lacked the supreme quality of the best ancient efforts, we must remember that few men have ever come as near to perfection as the best of the Greeks. On the other hand, if we place them in their own environment and compare the Arabic with other medieval efforts, the immense superiority of the former is obvious. We may say that from the middle of the eighth century to the end of the eleventh, the Arabic-speaking peoples (including within their ranks, it is true, a number of Jews and Christians) were march-

ing at the head of mankind. Thanks to them Arabic became
not only the sacred language of the Qur'ān, the vehicle of God's
own thoughts, but the international language of science, the
vehicle of human progress. Just as to-day the shortest way to
knowledge for any Oriental is the mastery of one of the main
occidental languages, even so during these four centuries Arabic
was the key, and almost the only key, to the new expanding
culture.

Indeed the superiority of Muslim culture, say in the eleventh
century, was so great that we can understand their intellectual
pride. It is easy to imagine their doctors speaking of the western
barbarians almost in the same spirit as ours do of the "Orientals."
If there had been some ferocious eugenists among the Muslims
they might have suggested some means of breeding out all the
western Christians and the Greeks because of their hopeless back-
wardness. At that time Muslim pride would have been the more
conceivable because they had almost reached their climax, and
pride is never so great as when the fall is near. On the contrary,
only a few Christians were then aware of their inferiority; that
awareness did not come upon them until much later—by the
middle of the thirteenth century—when Islām was already on the
downward path and Latin Christendom was climbing higher and
higher. This is very interesting, but the rule rather than the excep-
tion; when people boast too much of their culture it means either
that it is so new that they have not yet grown accustomed to it
or else that it is already decadent and that they try to hide their
incompetence (even from themselves) under the cloak of past
achievements. In the thirteenth century Islām was in the decadent
and boasting stage, while Christendom had finally realized the
richness of the Greco-Arabic knowledge and made gigantic efforts
to be allowed to share it, and hence was relatively in a chastened
mood.

For the sake of illustration let us consider the levels of mathematical knowledge among Muslims and among Christians in the
first half of the eleventh century. There was then a splendid

mathematical school in Cairo, made famous by the great astronomer, Ibn Yūnus and the great physicist Ibn al-Haitham; al-
Karkhī was working in Baghdād, Ibn Sīnā in Persia, al-Bīrūnī in
Afghānistān. These mathematicians and others, like Ibn al-Ḥusain
and Abū-l-Jūd, were not afraid to tackle the most difficult problems of Greek geometry; they solved cubic equations by the
intersection of conics, they investigated the regular heptagon and
enneagon, developed spherical trigonometry, Diophantine analysis, etc. Pass to the West and what do we find? Wretched little
treatises on the calendar, on the use of the abacus, on Roman
(duodecimal) fractions, etc. We have a "mathematical" cor-
respondence exchanged (c. 1025) by two schoolmasters, Ragim-
bold of Cologne and Radolf of Liége. It is truly pitiful. Their
geometry was on the pre-Pythagorean level; they were not bad
computers, it is true; we might compare them to the Egyptian
scribe Aḥmôse, who had done his task almost twenty-seven
centuries before!

How is it that the Muslim or oriental supremacy ended about
the end of the eleventh century? There was a double cause for
this: the Arabic genius was less vigorous and less fertile; the
power and knowledge of the Latin world was growing faster and
faster. The Arabic achievements did not stop, not by any means.
Great Arabic scientists and scholars continued to appear until
the fourteenth century and even later. For example, mathematicians and astronomers like Jābir ibn Aflaḥ, al-Biṭrūjī, al-
Ḥasan al-Marrākushī, Nāṣir al-Dīn al-Ṭūsī; physicists like
al-Khāzinī, Quṭb al-Dīn al-Shīrāzī, Kamāl al-Dīn ibn Yūnus;
geographers like Yāqūt, al-Qazwīnī, Abū-l-Fidā', Ibn Baṭṭūṭa;
philosophers like Ibn Rushd, Fakhr al-Dīn al-Rāzī, 'Abd al-Laṭīf;
physicians like Ibn Zuhr and Ibn al-Baiṭār; botanists and agri-
culturists like Ibn al-Ṣūrī and Ibn al-'Awwām; historians like
Ibn Khallikān, Rashīd al-Dīn, Ibn Khaldūn, al-Maqrīzī, etc., etc.
This list might be lengthened considerably and yet contain only
very distinguished names; as it is, it includes some of the most

illustrious ones in the whole history of civilization. The men I
have mentioned hailed from every part of Islām; a few of them
wrote in Persian, but even for those Arabic was a privileged language. Yet by the end of the eleventh century the main task of
the Arabic scientists—as far as it concerned the whole world and
not only themselves—was already completed, and after that time
the relative importance of Muslim culture declined steadily. During the twelfth century its prestige was due even more to its past
than to its present achievements, great as these were. In the meanwhile, Christians and Jews were feverishly pouring out the Greco-
Arabic learning from the Arabic vessels into the Latin and Hebrew
ones.

The Christians were far ahead of the Jews in this new stage
of transmission, and that for a very simple reason. Down to the
eleventh century the philosophic and scientific (as opposed to
the purely rabbinical) activities of the Jews were almost exclusively confined to the Muslim world. The Jewish philosophers,
grammarians, and scientists who lived under the protection of
Islām were generally well treated, and some of them—like Ḥasdai
ibn Shaprut in Cordova—attained positions of high authority and
became the intellectual as well as the political leaders of their
time. These Jews of the Dār al-Islām were bilingual; Hebrew was
of course their religious language and probably also their domestic one, but for all philosophic and scientific purposes they
thought in Arabic. They had no need of translations. On the
contrary it was much easier for them to read a medical book in
Arabic than in Hebrew. Sometimes they would copy Arabic manuscripts in Hebrew script, but even that was not really indispensable; it was more a matter of convenience than of necessity.

On the other hand, as soon as the Latin Christians began to
realize the importance of the Arabic literature, since only a few of
them could ever hope to master a language as alien to their own
and written in such illegible and mystifying script, they longed for
translations and did all they could to obtain them. By the end of
the eleventh century their longing was partly fulfilled by Con-

stantine the African, aptly called "magister orientis et occidentis";
he was indeed one of the great intermediaries between the East
and the West. Constantine translated a large number of Greco-
Muslim works from Arabic into Latin at the monastery of Monte
Cassino, where he died in 1087. As we might expect, the results
of his activity, far from appeasing the hunger of European
scholars, stimulated it considerably. It now dawned upon the
most advanced of them that the Arabic writings were not simply
important but essential, for they contained vast treasures of
knowledge, the accumulated learning and experience of the whole
past. It is no exaggeration to say that during the twelfth century
and down to about the middle of the thirteenth century, the fore-
most activity of Christian scholars was the translation of Arabic
treatises into Latin. There appeared a succession of translators of
such size that they have almost the dignity of creators: Adelard
of Bath, John of Seville, Domingo Gundisalvo, and many others
including the greatest of all times, Gerard of Cremona. By the
end of the twelfth century, the main body of Greco-Arabic knowledge was already available to Latin readers, but the more they
had, the more they wanted. By the end of the following century,
and even by the middle of it, there was little of real importance
in the Arabic scientific literature which they were not aware of.
Moreover, under the stimulus of the Arabic writings, some translators took pains to rediscover the Greek originals, and their
translations straight from the Greek followed closely upon the
heels of those from the Arabic. A remarkable case is that of the
Almagest. This was actually translated from the Greek before
being translated from the Arabic; the direct translation was made
in Sicily about 1160, the indirect one was completed by Gerard of
Cremona at Toledo in 1175. Yet such was the strength of the
Arabic tradition and Gerard's own prestige, that the earlier version, though presumably better, was entirely superseded by the
second.

At first the eastern Jews and those of Spain were much better
off than the Christians, for the whole of Arabic literature was

open to them without effort. But in the twelfth century the scientific life of Judaism began to move from Spain across the Pyrenees, and in the following century it began to decline in its former haunts. By the middle of the thirteenth century a great many Jews had already been established so long in France, Germany, and England, that Arabic had become a foreign language to them. Up to this period the Jews had been generally ahead of the Christians, and far ahead; now for the first time the situation was reversed. Indeed, the Christians had already transferred most of the Arabic knowledge into Latin; the translations from Arabic into Hebrew were naturally far less abundant, and hence the non-Arabic-speaking Jews of Western Europe were not only in a position of political inferiority (the Crusades had caused many anti-Semitic persecutions and the Jews of Christendom were everywhere on the defensive) but also—and this was perhaps even more painful—in a position of intellectual inferiority. To be sure, this was soon compensated by the fact that many of them learned Latin and could then read the Arabic texts in their Latin versions, but even then they no longer held an intellectual monopoly with regard to the Christians; they came but second. While the early Jewish physicians had possessed "secrets" of learning which were sealed to their Christian colleagues (this was especially true with regard to eye-diseases which were thoroughly investigated in Arabic treatises), the later ones had no such privileges. The gravity of the change is well illustrated by the appearance in the fourteenth and following centuries of an increasing number of translations (e.g., of medical works) from Latin into Hebrew. Thus the stream of translations which had been running from East to West was again reversed in the opposite direction. Note that a curious cycle had been completed, for the source of these writings was Greek; their Arabic elaborations had been translated into Latin and had inspired new Latin treatises; these treatises were now translated into Hebrew. From East to East via the West! But other cycles were even more curious. In the fourteenth century and later, Arabic, Persian, and Latin writings which were ultimately of Greek origin were re-translated into Greek. For example, the most popular logical textbook of the Middle Ages, the *Summulæ logicales* of Peter of Spain (Pope John XXI), was not only translated into Hebrew, but also into the very language from which its main sustenance had been indirectly derived. From Greek to Greek via Arabic and Latin!

Incidentally, this will help the reader to realize the usefulness of studying ancient translations. These give us the best means of appreciating the relative levels of various civilizations at definite periods. We can watch their rise and fall and, so to say, measure them. Streams of knowledge are constantly passing from one civilization into the others, and in the intellectual, even as in the material world, streams do not run upward. From a single translation one could deduce nothing, for its occurrence might be erratic. In the past even as now it was not necessarily the best writings which were translated; indeed some of the worst enjoyed that distinction more than any others. But if we consider the whole mass of translations, we can reconstruct the cultural exchanges and draw conclusions of the greatest interest. To return to my comparison of mankind with a single man, the activity of translators helps us to evoke the intellectual evolution of the former: we can tell which was the dominating influence at each time, and, so to say, retrace his wandering steps across the schools and the academies of the old world.

During the twelfth century the three civilizations which exerted the deepest influence upon human thought and which had the largest share in the molding of the future, the Jewish, the Christian, and the Muslim, were remarkably well balanced; but that state of equilibrium could not last very long, because it was due to the fact that the Muslims were going down while the two others were going up. By the end of the twelfth century it was already clear (that is, it would have been clear to any outside observer, as it is to ourselves) that the Muslims would soon be out of the race, and that the competition would be restricted to the Christians and the Jews. Now the latter were hopelessly jeopardized by their political servitude and by the jealous intolerance and the utter lack of generosity (to put it mildly!) of their rivals. Moreover, for the reason explained above, the main sources of knowledge were now less available to them than to their persecutors. This went much deeper than it seems, for when an abundant treasure of knowledge becomes suddenly available to a group of people, it is not only the knowledge itself that matters, but the stimulation following in its wake. The Jews were steadily driven into the background, and in proportion as they were more isolated, they tended to increase their isolation by devoting their attention more exclusively to their own Talmudic studies.

Toward the end of the thirteenth century some of the greatest doctors of Christendom, Albert the Great, Roger Bacon, Ramon Lull, were ready to acknowledge the many superiorities of Arabic culture. It is paradoxical but not surprising that at the very time when that full realization had come to them, that culture was already declining, and their own was finally triumphing. From that time on, the Christians enjoyed the political and intellectual hegemony. The center of gravity of the learned world was in the West and it has remained there until our own days; by a strange irony of fate it may even pass some day beyond the western ocean which was then supposed to be an insuperable barrier. Moreover, because of the decadence and fall of Muslim Spain and of the growing isolation and aloofness of the Jews, the West became more and more westernized. Of course Muslim and Jewish efforts went on and both faiths produced many great men in the following centuries, yet the western supremacy continued to wax until a time was reached, in the sixteenth century, when the expanding civilization was so deeply westernized that the people—even those of the Orient—began to forget its oriental origins, and when the very conception of Muslim and Jewish science almost disappeared. That conception may seem artificial to us, but I believe I have made it clear enough that it was a perfectly natural and necessary one in medieval times. The final results of science are, of course, independent of the people who discovered them, but we are anxious to find out how much we owe to each of them, in what kind of environment knowledge developed, and which devious ways the human spirit followed throughout the ages. After the sixteenth century, when science was finally disentangled from theology, the distinction between Jewish, Christian, and Muslim science ceased to be justified, but it keeps its historical value. In spite of his deep Jewishness and of his abundant use of Jewish sources, we do not count Spinoza any more as a Jewish philosopher in the same sense that we count Maimonides or Levi ben Gershon; he is one of the founders of modern philosophy, one of the noblest representatives of the human mind, not eastern or western, but the two unified.

Perhaps the main, as well as the least obvious, achievement of the Middle Ages, was the creation of the experimental spirit, or more exactly, its slow incubation. This was primarily due to Muslims down to the end of the twelfth century, then to Christians. Thus in this essential respect, East and West coöperated like brothers. However much one may admire Greek science, one must recognize that it was sadly deficient with regard to this (the experimental) point of view which turned out to be the fundamental point of view of modern science. Though their great physicians instinctively followed experimental methods, these methods were never properly appreciated by their philosophers or by the students of nature. A history of Greek experimental science, outside of medicine, would be exceedingly short. Under the influence of Arabic alchemists and opticians, and later of Christian mechanicians and physicists, the experimental spirit grew very slowly. For centuries it remained very weak, comparable to a delicate little plant, always in danger of being ruthlessly trampled down by dogmatic theologians and conceited philosophers. The tremendous awakening due to the western re-discovery of printing and to the exploration of the new world, accelerated its development. By the beginning of the sixteenth century it was already lifting its head up, and we may consider

Leonardo da Vinci its first deliberate vindicator. After that, its progress became more and more rapid, and, by the beginning of the following century, experimental philosophy was admirably explained by another Tuscan, Galileo, the herald of modern science.

Thus if we take a very broad view of the history of science, we may distinguish in it four main phases. The first is the empirical development of Egyptian and Mesopotamian knowledge. The second is the building of a rational foundation of astounding beauty and strength by the Greeks. The third, and until recently the least known, is the medieval period—many centuries of groping. Immense efforts were spent to solve pseudo-problems, chiefly to conciliate the results of Greek philosophy with religious dogmas of various kinds. Such efforts were naturally sterile, as far as their main object was concerned, but they brought into being many incidental results. The main result, as I have just explained, was the incubation of the experimental spirit. Its final emergence marks the transition between the third period and the fourth, which is the period of modern science. Note that out of these four periods the first is entirely oriental, the third is mostly but not exclusively so; the second and fourth are exclusively western.

To return to the fourth period—which is still continuing—the final establishment of the experimental philosophy was indeed its main distinction, its standard, and its glory. Not only did the new method open the path to untold and unimaginable discoveries, but it put an end to unprofitable quests and idle discussions; it broke the vicious circles wherein philosophers had been obstinately turning for more than a thousand years. It was simple enough in itself, but could not be understood as long as a series of intellectual prejudices obscured man's vision. It may be summed up as follows: Establish the facts by direct, frequent, and careful observations, and check them repeatedly one against the other; these facts will be your premises. When many variables are related, find out what happens when only one is allowed to vary, the others remaining constant. Multiply such experiments as much as you can, and make them with the utmost precision in your power. Draw your conclusions and express them in mathematical language if possible. Apply all your mathematical resources to the transformation of the equations; confront the new equations thus obtained with reality. That is, see what they mean, which group of facts they represent. Make new experiments on the basis of these new facts, etc., etc.

All the triumphs of modern science have been due to the application, more or less deliberate, of that method. Moreover experimental scientists have laid more and more emphasis on the needs of objective verification. Truth is relative but it becomes less and less so, and more and more reliable, in proportion as it has been checked oftener and in a greater variety of ways. The experimental method, simple as it may seem to anyone who approaches it with an open mind, developed only very gradually. Little by little, scientists learned by experience to trust their reason more than their feelings, but also not to trust their reason too much. The results of any argument, just like the results of any mathematical transformation, are not entirely valid until they have been checked and re-checked in many ways. Facts can only be explained by theories, but they can never be explained away; thus, however insignificant in themselves, they remain supreme. They are like the stones of a building; individual stones are worthless but the building would have no reality without them.

It is amusing to hear the old humanists speak of restraint and discipline as if they had the monopoly of these qualities, when the experimental method is itself the most elaborate discipline of thought which has ever been conceived. To be sure, it does not apply to everything; nor does it claim any monopoly for itself except within its own domain.

It is the experimental method which has given to human reason its full potency, but at the same time it has clearly shown its limitations and provided means of controlling it. It has proved the relativity of truth, but at the same time has made it possible to measure its objectivity and its degree of approximation. Above all it has taught men to be impartial (or at least to try to be), to want the whole truth, and not only the part of it which may be convenient or agreeable. Such impartiality was obviously impossible, and almost inconceivable, so long as the objectivity of truth could not be appreciated.

The experimental method is in appearance the most revolutionary of all methods. Does it not lead to astounding discoveries and inventions? Does it not change the face of the world so deeply and so often that superficial people think of it as the very spirit of change? And yet it is essentially conservative, for it hesitates to draw conclusions until their validity has been established and verified in many ways; it is so cautious that it often gives an impression of timidity. It seems revolutionary because it is so efficient; its conclusions, because of their restraint, cannot be opposed; because of their strength they cannot be frustrated. When thought is as severely disciplined as scientific thought, it is irresistible, and yet it is the greatest element of stability in the world. How shall we account for that paradox? Progress implies stability; it implies the respect of traditions. Scientific thought is, or seems, revolutionary because the consequences it leads to are so great and often unexpected, but it leads to them in a steady way. The history of science describes an evolution of incomparable magnitude which gives us a very high idea of man's intellectual power, but this evolution is as steady as that which is caused by natural forces.

You have heard the story of the cowboy who, coming suddenly upon the rim of the Grand Cañon, exclaimed: "Good Lord, something has happened here!" Now, as you know, the cowboy was wrong if he meant that something had happened at a definite time, and had been rapidly completed. In that sense nothing ever happened in the Grand Cañon. In the same way the development of science, though incomparably swifter than the cutting of a cañon, is a steady process; it seems revolutionary, because we do not really see the process, but only the gigantic results.

From the point of view of experimental science, especially in its present stage of development, the opposition between East and West seems extreme. However—and this is the burden of my essay —we must bear in mind two things.

The first is that the seeds of science, including the experimental method and mathematics, in fact, the seeds of all the forms of science, came from the East; and that during the Middle Ages they were largely developed by Eastern people. Thus, in a large sense, experimental science is a child not only of the West, but also of the East; the East was its mother, the West was its father.

In the second place, I am fully convinced that the West still needs the East to-day, as much as the East needs the West. As soon as the Eastern peoples have unlearned their scholastic and argumentative methods, as we did in the sixteenth century, as soon as they are truly inspired with the experimental spirit, there is no telling what they may be able to do for us, or (heaven forbid!) against us. To be sure, as far as scientific research is concerned they could only work with us, but their applications of it might be very different. We must not make the same mistake as the Greeks who thought for centuries that their spirit was the only one, who ignored altogether the Semitic spirit and considered foreign people barbarians; their ultimate fall was as deep as their triumph had been high. Remember the rhythm between East and West; many times already has our inspiration come from the East; why should that never happen again? The chances are that great ideas will still reach us from the East and we must be ready to welcome them.

The men who assume a truculent attitude against the East and make the most extravagant claims for the Western civilization, are not likely to be scientists. Most of them have neither knowledge nor understanding of science; that is, they do not in the least deserve the superiority of which they boast so much and which their incoherent desires would soon extinguish, if they were left to themselves.

We are justly proud of our American civilization, but its records are still very short. Three centuries! How little that is as compared with the totality of human experience; hardly more than a moment, a wink of the eye. Will it last? Will it improve or wane and die out? There are many unhealthy elements in it and if we wish to uproot them before the disease has spread beyond our control, we must expose them mercilessly, but that is not my task. If we want our civilization to justify itself, we must do our best to purify it. One of the best ways of doing this is the cultivation of disinterested science; the love of truth—as a scientist loves it, the whole of it, pleasant or unpleasant, useful or not; the love of truth, not the fear of it; the hatred of superstition, no matter how beautiful its disguises may be. Whether our civilization will last or not, at any rate it has not yet proved its longevity. Hence we must be modest. After all the main test is that of survival, and we have not yet been tried.

New inspirations may still, and do still, come from the East, and we shall be wiser if we realize it. In spite of its prodigious triumphs, the scientific method is not all-sufficient. It is supreme when it can be applied and when it is well applied, but it would be foolish not to recognize the two kinds of limitations which this implies. First, the method cannot always be applied. There are immense realms of thought where it is thus far inapplicable—art, religion, morality. Perhaps it will always be inapplicable to them. Second, it can be very easily misapplied, and the possibilities of misapplication of such an inexhaustible source of power are appalling.

It is clear that the scientific spirit is unable to control its own applications. To begin with, these applications are often in the hands of people who have no scientific knowledge whatever; for example, it is not necessary to have any education or instruction in order to drive a high-powered car which may cause any amount of destruction. But even scientists might be tempted to misapply their knowledge under the influence of a strong passion. The scientific spirit must be itself assisted by other forces of a different kind—by religion and morality. In any case, it must not be arrogant, nor aggressive, for it is like all other things human, essentially imperfect.

The unity of mankind includes East and West. They are like two moods of the same man; they represent two fundamental and complementary phases of human experience. Scientific truth is the same East and West, and so are beauty and charity. Man is the same everywhere with a little more emphasis on this or that.

East and West, who said the twain shall never meet? They meet in the soul of every great artist who is more than an artist and whose love is not restricted to beauty; they meet also in the soul of every great scientist who has been brought to realize that truth, however precious, is not the whole of life, that it must be completed by beauty and charity.

Let us remember with gratitude all that we owe to the East—the moral earnestness of Judea, the Golden Rule, the very rudiments of the science we are so proud of—this is an immense debt. There is no reason why it should not be indefinitely increased in the future. We must not be too sure of ourselves; our science may be great, our ignorance is greater still. By all means let us develop our methods, improve our intellectual discipline, continue our scientific work, slowly, steadily, in a humble spirit; but at the same time let us be charitable and ever mindful of all the beauty which surrounds us, of all the grace which is in our fellowmen and perhaps in ourselves. Let us destroy the things which are evil, the ugliness which mars our dwelling places, the injustice which we do to others, above all, the lies which cover all sins; but let us beware of destroying or hurting even the smallest of the many things which are good and innocent. Let us defend our traditions, all the memories of our past, which are our most valuable heritage.

To see things as they are—by all means! But the highest aspirations of my soul, my nostalgia for things unseen, my hunger for beauty and justice, these are also realities and precious ones. The many things which are beyond my grasp are not necessarily unreal. We must always be ready to reach out for these intangible realities which give to our life its nobility and its ultimate direction.

Ex oriente lux, ex occidente lex. Let us discipline our souls, and be loyal to objective truth, yet heedful of every phasis of reality, whether tangible or not. The scientist who is not too proud, who does not assume an aggressively "western" attitude, but remembers the eastern origin of his highest thoughts, who is not ashamed of his ideals—will not be more efficient, but he will be more humane, a better servant of the truth, a better instrument of destiny, a gentler man.

PART FOUR

CASTING BREAD UPON THE WATERS

10. AN INSTITUTE FOR THE HISTORY OF SCIENCE AND CIVILIZATION

There has been much talk in recent years of the need of humanizing science, but nothing has been done on a sufficient scale to satisfy that need. Large endowments are found for the creation of new laboratories and observatories, but the relatively small endowment needed for historical and humanistic purposes is apparently unavailable. There is plenty of money for instruments of increasing cost, but no money is available to make sure that the men using these instruments will remain sufficiently educated. Putting it bluntly, a certain percentage (say 5%) of the scientific budget should be devoted to the humanization of science as an insurance against its gradual barbarization. Scientific studies and teaching are so lop-sided on the purely technical side that a healthy balance cannot be restored by pious exhortations and half-hearted measures.

Secular continuity—The most disheartening feature of historical work to-day is the frequent replacement of older books by newer ones which are less good and give a new currency to old errors. This is due to the inexperience of many historians of science, to the historical dilettantism of some distinguished scientists, and above all to the lack of standards.

The best way to cure these evils is slowly to produce accounts of the history of science as comprehensive and accurate as possible, and sufficiently massive to justify the publication of periodical errata and addenda, and from time to time of new editions incorporating the accumulated improvements. My *Introduction to the History of Science* and *Isis* are good but insufficient beginnings in that direction. I cannot do more, though I am desperately straining all my energy and every resource in the effort, because I am not sufficiently supported.

Indeed such accurate and systematic work is slow, tedious, difficult and austere; also expensive, though in the long run it is far more economical than fast and inaccurate work, which is unreliable and ephemeral.

The establishment of the history of science as I understand it, is a *secular* undertaking; it cannot be realized except by the coöperation of successive generations of disciplined scholars working together quietly, humbly, without undue haste but without cease. To illustrate, consider two other secular undertakings. The Jesuits, Heribert Rosweyde (d. 1629) and John Bolland (d.1665) organized the study of hagiology. The first volume of the *Acta sanctorum* appeared in 1643; the work has been continued ever since by a devoted band of scholars called Bollandists; it is not yet completed. At the beginning of the eighteenth century, Dom Antoine Rivet de la Grange and other Benedictines of the Congregation of St. Maur undertook to write the history of French literature on a scientific basis. The first volume appeared in 1733; in 1807 the work was continued by the Académie des Inscriptions; they have now reached the fourteenth century.

The work I have undertaken, the writing of the history of science and learning, the history of the development of objective knowledge of every kind in every country at every time, is much broader in scope than either of these two examples. Its completion will be far more difficult, and will involve the coöperation of many generations of scholars. Our main task is to train the first group of scholars and to establish sound traditions.

Need of an Institute—It is because this project is *secular* that an *Institute* is needed. As it is beyond the grasp of a single scholar, or of a single generation, its organization must be intrusted to a body of scholars, in order that the work may be continued and indefinitely perfected. I hope that at the time of its Fourth Centenary, Harvard University may find within its orbit an Institute of the History of Science and Learning in full swing, continuing its immense task with extreme care and reasonable speed. By that time it may already have produced a few standard works, and thus have raised the level of historiography throughout the world.

The Institute would consist of a staff of experts using the apparatus criticus bequeathed to them by earlier colleagues and gradually enriched by themselves, and following definite traditions of scholarship subject to continuous selection and improvement. The men come first to be sure, but the best men cannot do their best without a very elaborate equipment, the preparation of which implies the uninterrupted devotion of many generations. Succeeding scholars do not gradually improve—the earlier ones may be better than their successors—but their equipment becomes better and richer and their traditions more exacting.

Strangely enough, while there are many similar institutes devoted to the history of art, or religion, or of other phases of culture, there is none really well equipped devoted to the history of science. There is no need of many such institutes, but there should be at least one, established preferably in or near one of the largest libraries, within the orbit of a great university.

Science and learning—Since the beginning of my efforts in 1912, my conception of science has been continually broadening. It now includes the whole of objective and verifiable knowledge. However, much of that knowledge is often classified under the heading of "learning" rather than that of "science," and "learned societies" are often opposed to "scientific societies" though their aim is essentially the same, to determine the most probable truth in their respective fields. President Conant's suggestion to speak of "science and learning" instead of science alone is thus very welcome; it helps to bring together scholars and scientists by making them realize their kinship. The history of science is enriched in many ways if it is made to include the history of learning.

East and West—Many scientists conceive the history of science only from their own western point of view, and do not realize how much of it is of eastern origin. That conception is not only incomplete but false. Western and eastern influences are complementary, and one cannot neglect the one or the other without loss of perspective. The antithesis East-and-West is somewhat comparable to the one considered in the previous section. Failure to take both sides into account (East *and* West, science *and* learning) implies the same intellectual distortions and shortcomings in either case.

Contemporary science—Even as the smallest institute should devote a part of its activities to the history of learning and to eastern thought lest it be unbalanced, even so provision should be made from the beginning for the study of contemporary science as well as of the earlier achievements. Contemporary science may be understood in general as nineteenth- and twentieth-century science; or more strictly as beginning in the nineties of the last century. Historians of science must be trained to interpret the present in terms of the past and vice-versa. However, the study of contemporary science implies the use of methods of a very different kind, the emphasis being necessarily laid on the selection of the most significant materials, rather than a study of all the materials —which would defeat its own purpose. Means must be taken to analyze gradually the scientific production of our time, and to prepare careful annals, without which the synthesis of later historians will hardly be possible. In a sense this task is more urgent than the others; it makes not much difference whether an exhaustive survey of fourteenth-century science is available in 1930 or 1950, but the philosophically- and historically-minded scientist of to-day should be able to review as easily as possible the efforts of his older contemporaries and to see them in their proper perspective.

Ethical trends—The members of the Institute would not be simply annalists and historians, but humanists. One of their main functions would be to interpret the ethical and social implications of science in all ages, and especially in our own, to integrate science into general education, in a word, to "humanize" science. This has been understood best by historians of medicine, and no wonder, medicine being more intimately concerned than any other science with every aspect of individual and social life. Thus in some universities students are taught in the same courses the history of medicine, medical deontology, and even social medicine.

It has been claimed that science is not concerned with moral issues. That may be true, yet scientists are members of the community and their aloofness is seldom excusable.

Some historians of science should be as well acquainted as possible with the history of religions, of ethics, and of social endeavors of every kind. It would be their special duty to harmonize the results of their inquiries with those concerning the history of science, and to help explain each in terms of the others.

Unification of good will—An Institute devoted, as this one, to the study of the most precious common good of mankind might be considered a clearing house of good will, irrespective of its origin. Its highest function would be to interpret, primarily but not exclusively in scientific terms, the development of culture; not the culture of any nation, race, faith, or profession but the culture of mankind. Indeed the ideals of humanity transcend immeasurably those of any group.

Defense of the scientific spirit and method—One of these universal ideals is the love of truth, and the disinterested search for it, irrespective of desires and consequences. The history of science is to a large extent a history of the liberation of thought, of the conflict between rationalism and superstition (not religion), of man's quest for truth and gradual approach to it, of his struggle against error and unreason.

Iconography—A department should be devoted to the collection of iconographic documents (e.g., portraits, medals) pertinent to the general purpose. This field of study would connect the Institute with art museums; in addition to the realization of a practical aim it would introduce a new point of view and a new form of humanism.

Physical organization—Details of organization need not be examined before the value of the Institute is understood and its general principles accepted, but a few generalities may help to complete this outline.

The ideal location of the Institute would be inside a large

library, the largest available. Indeed the historian of science may be called upon to consult almost every kind of book or periodical, not only scientific but many others as well. However, such a location may be impossible to obtain or to retain, for an Institute growing within a Library would easily conflict with the latter. The next best location would be in a modest but extensible building, close to a very large library.

The building should be large enough to accommodate a reference library, the apparatus criticus (pamphlets, MSS, portraits, etc.), offices for members, reading rooms for students and visitors, a seminar room and perhaps a lecture room. It should be as beautiful as possible, which does not mean luxurious or expensive. Though open to every *bona fide* student, it should not be a show place. The best comparison, perhaps, is with an observatory, where astronomical data are patiently accumulated for immediate and secular use. In this Institute historical data would be collected, classified and interpreted, historical methods improved, humanistic traditions guarded, enriched, and transmitted.

Staff—The staff would include the director, librarian and archivist, and scholars of three grades: senior fellows, junior fellows and apprentices. In the selection of fellows and students one would have to take into account, on the one hand, the diverse needs of the Institute (e.g., science vs. learning, East vs. West, contemporary vs. ancient science) and on the other hand, the men available. Some fundamental needs (e.g., the care of the library and archives) should be satisfied at once, while the other departments would be allowed to grow according to the opportunities.

11. CASTING BREAD UPON THE FACE OF THE WATERS

A good many years ago when I was a student in Ghent, I spent a holiday with my father in Holland, travelling from place to place across the little kingdom. One night we landed in the island of Texel, and I was at first horrified by its bleakness. At the inn we met two Dutch girls who told us they were spending the *whole* summer in Texel; they were collecting plants, resting, and having a good time, so they said. The *whole* summer in that God-forsaken place! I was a conceited young ass in those days (I am quite sure that whatever else I may be I am no longer a conceited young ass), and the quiet extravagance of these two girls seemed very funny to me. Years afterwards it occurred to me that they had far better grounds for chaffing me than I them, and that sobering thought has come back to me many times since, but never with greater strength than at the time when I was gazing at the sea from the Santa Cruz Mountains of Jamaica, across the Pedro plains.

Texel had a message for these two girls which I was too immature to grasp. I blamed Texel, but the blame came back upon me like a boomerang. When we travel we create everywhere a new environment of which we are an essential part; wherever we may go we meet ourselves more often than other people. I found nothing in Texel because I went there with empty hands. The bleakness of the place was partly the bleakness of my own ignorance. I have learned a few things since then, and to-day should I be a little hasty in condemning things which I do not know, I have but to whisper to my soul "Texel," and I stop and ponder. On the other hand, when other people belittle my activity without trying to find out what I am driving at, or adjudge me a

fool simply because they have not taken the trouble of understanding me, I say to myself "Texel" and smile it off.

I used to worry a good deal because so many students do not
really understand my lectures. Out of an average number of
students I hardly expect more than two or three to take a genuine
interest in them. Is it worthwhile? I sometimes thought it was a
waste of time, but I think differently now. Even if I could not
reach more than two or three minds each year the effort would
be justified, but it is probable that my lectures reach many more
who are not yet aware of it then and there, but will realize it later
elsewhere. Did it not take me a long time to grasp the simple
Texel message? Should the blindness, deafness, and inertia of my
own youth not warn and help me to be patient with others? Obviously those students are still in Texel, but some of them will eventually sail to Jamaica.

What is perhaps more irritating and disheartening than plain
ignorance is that so many of them get to know the facts of the
course but miss its spirit. Of course we should know a number
of facts, though nobody can be expected to retain them as faithfully as does a good book. I myself do not try to remember the
facts of my own lectures except in a general way. The essential
is their main purpose, and this is often misunderstood even by the
students who know the details best. In every examination I include among the more technical questions at least one very broad
question, such as this: "Why on earth did you take my course?"
and it pains me to discover how few students are able to answer
the broader questions in a satisfactory manner. Their papers show
that they have studied the course, but somehow they have failed
to grasp its meaning. They have carefully gathered all the husks
and lost the seeds.

What then is the purpose? The immediate purpose is to explain
the development of scientific ideas—in time and space—the gradual elaboration of theories and of new branches of science: the

growth of the whole tree and its growing complexity and splendor. The technical aspects of this are obvious, the purely human, less so but hardly less important. That development is a part of the history of mankind, not an incidental but an essential part; it gives us opportunities of illustrating man's inherent greatness and goodness, the gradual realization of his highest destiny, the slow unfolding and revealing of the best in him. The purpose is to bring scientists and humanists more closely together by explaining to the latter the inward meaning of scientific discoveries (not simply their outward usefulness), and to the former their deep humanity; it is to educate the barbarians in our midst, not the least of whom are those technicians and scientists who, however expert in their own pursuits, fail to harmonize science with life and art and to appreciate human values.

Once, long ago, when Fan Ch'ih asked the meaning of virtue, the Master (Confucius) replied "Love your fellow men." Upon his asking the meaning of knowledge, the Master said: "Know your fellow men." Our modern definition of knowledge or of science—which is simply organized knowledge—is much broader, but it is possible that in the process of broadening it, the essential has been lost. For that essential: is it not the same as it was in Confucius' days, two and a half millennia ago? However abstract our knowledge may be, and however hard we may try to eliminate subjective elements, it is still in the last analysis intensely human. Everything which we think or do is relative to man. Science is nothing but the reflection of nature in a human mirror. We may improve the mirror indefinitely; and though we may rid it, or ourselves, of one cause of error after another, it is and will always be, for good or for evil, irremediably human.

Now it is one thing to purify our theories and our instruments, to increase their abstraction, their generality, their invariance, and to minimize to the limit of our ability the disturbing and erratic elements, especially those introduced by our own personalities; it is quite another to appraise the human meaning and value of those theories and instruments. In the first case, we consider the matter from the technical and practical point of view; in the second, we consider it from the purely human one. There is no conflict, for the generalization and abstraction are made by men and for men; both points of view are not opposite or exclusive; on the contrary they complete one another. The second is essentially that of the historian of science. It is not only legitimate but necessary if we wish to integrate science into our culture and not use it only as an instrument foreign to it.

Historians of science like other specialists are so busy, so deeply immersed in their own activity, that they have no time to think about it, to consider it as it were from the outside, and they run the risk of adding new misunderstandings: namely, these two capital ones: the exaggerated value accorded to scientific progress on the one hand, and the underestimation of progress in other fields.

Let us examine the second first, for it is perhaps the more common as well as the more blatant. The reality of social progress is not only underestimated but often called into question. Are we better—morally and socially—than our ancestors; is the body politic of which we are units healthier? There are plenty of reasons to make us doubt it. The organization of good activities may be steadily improving, but the organization of vicious ones is also improving, and one may well wonder: which side is gaining?

Virtues and vices are as old as mankind but their forms and combinations vary: are the modern forms better or worse? Is any advance in the right direction tangible enough, and other than precarious? Our suspicions and fears cannot be quelled for very long. Consider war: though the number of wars may be steadily decreasing (is it really?) their size is increasing. Where is the gain? If there be social progress it is exceedingly slow, interrupted by many vicissitudes, and jeopardized by many retrogressions. However, is our impatience justified? Beginning with ancient Egypt and Mesopotamia we have some sixty centuries of recorded experience: this may seem very much; it is in reality very little—only about two hundred generations. (Thomas Hunt Morgan and his school have already been able to study a far larger number of generations of the fruit fly, *Drosophila melanogaster!*) Yet it is not even necessary to consider the whole sweep of history to realize that the progress, however slow, is tangible. To be sure, it is never so certain and irrevocable as the progress in the discovery of truth, but its precariousness itself decreases gradually.

To illustrate the reality of a change for the better let us go back only a few generations to the middle of the eighteenth century and to the city which was then the main center of culture in the world: Paris. The French "society" of that time was exceedingly polite and elegant. Nowhere in that age did the refinements of life reach a higher pitch. Well and good. Let us repair to the Place de grève, on March 28, 1757. A large crowd has gathered there to witness a very exciting spectacle: a criminal being tortured to death. There had been such competition to hire the windows overlooking the square, that some people paid as much as twelve louis for a single one. What was the occasion of that extraordinary entertainment?

On January 5 of the same year, a jobless servant named Damiens, had a chance of approaching Louis XV at Versailles and stabbed him with a knife. The wound was slight. The man was obviously a monomaniac. He explained that his purpose had not been to kill the king but to *touch* and *warn* him. This crime excited deep emotion and horror, for in spite of the king's viciousness and insane profligacy which were well known, he was still in the eyes of the multitude a *sacred* person. Damiens was submitted to frequent tortures for more than two months. The refinements of medieval cruelty were found insufficient and a new kind of rack was introduced from Avignon for his supplice. All this to no avail, for he confessed nothing;—the poor devil had nothing to confess except the crime itself which had been public. Finally he was condemned to be quartered alive and the execution was fixed for the 28th of March. It was arranged that the show be as long as possible, and the society people who hired windows knew that they would get their money's worth. The poorer spectators had to stand in the square or lose their places, but the richer ones would retire to the rooms whenever there was an intermezzo and play cards. The intermezzi were needed to enable the prisoner to recruit his strength for the next turn. The Count de Tocqueville remarks: "La plume se refuse à retracer les effroyables détails des souffrances d'un malheureux insensé sur lesquels les bourreaux s'acharnèrent pendant plusieures heures." On the morning of that fateful day Damiens was submitted to a final torture in the "chambre de la question," and it was carried to within an inch of his life, being discontinued only when the physicians and surgeons declared that death was dangerously near. This torture having been as fruitless as the preceding ones it was decided to proceed with the punishment. Damiens was entrusted to the clergy for the care of his soul, and then carried to the Place de grève more dead than alive.

However ghastly and shocking these tortures were to any normal person, what is far more shocking is the fact that so many people of fashion found pleasure and excitement in them. In this crucial respect that extra-refined Parisian society was on the same level as the Iroquois Indians whose delight it was to prolong the sufferings of their victims—on the same level as those untutored savages but with no excuse.

The admirable elegance of the eighteenth century was indeed, as measured by later standards, only a veneer, concealing the most disgusting license and brutality, not only in the underworld but in the upper one, in the very highest spheres, even in the sphere of royalty which was generally supposed to be almost divine. The damning point is that the evil conduct of royalty and nobility was well known to the multitude, and yet the authors of such misdeeds were not disgraced (as they would certainly be to-day) but honored and even adored. Louis XV was called "Le bien aimé," the Beloved! There are plenty of brutes and swine among our own contemporaries, but they have to hide themselves very carefully.

Exposure would throw them back into the mud where they belong.

I admit that there were also many noble men and women, whose nobility appeared not only in their coats of arms but in their character and conduct, and who were able to enjoy all the elegances of the age and at the same time to exemplify its finest virtues. But even at best, that society was extremely limited, and the famous "douceur de vivre" of the eighteenth century of which some of our literary men and artists are dreaming as if it were the supreme reward of a golden age, cannot have been more common then than it is now. In fact, life was so far from sweet for the masses that they were finally goaded into the despair of revolt. Revolutions, it should be noted, do not happen without cause or reason; they are generally the result of a long preparation—not of years but of centuries; and those who prepare them are not the revolutionaries, the so-called leaders, but rather the privileged people who abuse their privileges and increase the burdens of the people beyond endurance.

We have abundant proofs of the cruelty, barbarism, and inhumanity of those times in the *Encyclopédie* (if one can read between the lines) and in the writings of the "philosophers." La Bruyère's description of the peasants had appeared in the preceding century (1688), but it was still as cruelly true in the eighteenth, for their condition hardly improved before the Revolution. Listen to this old English version of it.

> We meet with certain wild Animals, Male and Female, spread over the Country, black and tann'd with the Sun, link'd down to the Earth, which they are always digging and turning up and down with an unweary'd Resolution; they have something like an articulate Voice, and when they stand erect discover a human Face, and indeed are Men; at Night they retire into their Burrows, where they live on brown Bread, Water, Roots and Herbs: They save other Men the trouble of sowing, labouring, and reaping for their Maintenance, and deserve, one would think, not to want the Bread they sow themselves.

Could a more terrible indictment be penned? Truly the "douceur de vivre" which some of the paintings and music of that time suggest, was restricted to a very small company. And could the nobler spirits of that age continue to enjoy that "sweetness" as soon as they realized the unlimited miseries and the degrading servitude of the majority of their neighbors?

In contrast with the rustics of La Bruyère, hopelessly crushed down below the level of humanity, I shall always recall with pleasure the black peasantry of Jamaica, whom I was privileged to observe during my stay in that beautiful country. Though they were still slaves less than a century ago, they have developed remarkably well. It is a joy to meet them along the ways and paths of the island, walking or riding with considerable dignity and greeting the stranger with courtesy. Even small children gave me appropriate salutations in good English. I attended a Nativity Play in Bethlehem College, a Moravian school for colored girls in Malvern, and was deeply touched by their gracious performance.

To be sure there is still a superabundance of misery, ignorance, and vice, even in our most enlightened communities, and it is better that we should always bear it in mind, and be very humble and penitent: when I derided the "douceur de vivre" of the eighteenth century and suggested that our times were better, I did not imply that they were "sweet." No kind person can truly enjoy life while he knows that so many of his fellowmen are wantonly ground under the wheels. The real meaning of that ancient "douceur de vivre" is that we may be excused if we forget the evils of the eighteenth century while we should never forget those which it is in our power to cure. However, the consciousness of our social imperfections should not hide from us another truth: the reality of social progress which any detailed comparison between the conditions of to-day and those of a thousand or a hundred years ago would reveal. We are still very far from the goal. This is the more offensive, because that goal is not an invisible one like the goal of science, but on the contrary plainly visible and attainable;—yet we are moving, be it ever so slowly, in the right direction.

On the other hand, there is perhaps too much boasting about the progress of knowledge, especially by those who are foreign to it and understand it least. The knowledge revealed by scientific research is undoubtedly wonderful; but the wonder does not necessarily increase with the size and complexity of the universe, and the latest achievements of science are not more marvelous (as achievements) than the earlier ones. Some simple-minded people exult because the universe of modern science is immeasurably larger than that of Ptolemy or even of Herschel, but it does not make such a great difference after all, if they continue to be such fools and humbugs. It is equally silly to disdain scientific endeavors or to overestimate them to the detriment of others, such as the creation of beauty or justice. The best fruit of these endeavors is not any definite result, but a new attitude of mind: the appreciation of truth. Veracity, complete and unrestricted, is a conquest of science, even of modern science, and earlier people could have no conception of it. It is significant that "to tell the truth" was not one of the Ten Commandments; it is more significant still that lying, or tampering in various ways or degrees with the truth is not yet the disgrace that it ought to be, except within the narrow scientific field. This shows that however deep and comprehensive our scientific knowledge may be, our scientific spirit is still very weak. The progress of veracity—which ought to be our measuring rod for the real scientific advance—is just as slow and precarious as social progress. Hence there is nothing much to boast about. It is clear that scientific enlightenment can purify life only to the extent that veracity favors its diffusion. All the social evils will eventually wither in the light of knowledge, but this can only happen when that light actually reaches them and is not screened off by our greed and hypocrisy.

Knowledge is not valuable in itself but in relation to other things. Like any other form of power, it may be (and often is) misused, in which case it is evil and dangerous. Without being misused it may be spoiled and made worthless and contemptible by the lack of charity or the excess of conceit. We must try to know things as they are: this is fundamental, but not final. There is a world of difference between what we know on the one hand, and what we are and do on the other. The perfect humanist must take all this into account.

We can only find ourselves by losing ourselves. This is in my opinion the deepest saying of the Gospels, without exact equivalent as far as I know in other Scriptures. There is much emphasis of course in other sacred writings, especially those of India, on the need of self abandonment to attain reality, but the implications are metaphysical and mystical rather than ethical. People who are always talking of metaphysical truth are just as likely as not to be inveterate liars. I am not very interested in the theories of knowledge; my concern is truthfulness as honest men and scientists understand it. Lawyers, theologians, and even philosophers may indulge in distinctions and equivocations and get away with it; scientists cannot do that without disgrace.

To return to Christ's saying, it is often misinterpreted; it is considered unworldly, and indeed the climax of unworldly wisdom and sanctity. To me it seems to be simply the expression of common sense. One may find verifications of it in almost every human life—in frustrated ambitions as well as in those whose very fulfillment could not conceal their vanity. The self-seeker finds nothing but his own poor self, and sundry trifles, such as wealth, to which his disorderly brain attaches a false value. He can reach nothing but the phantoms of his own imagination, and this would not matter so much if he did not abandon, for the sake of reaching them, precious realities. It is not necessary to search for the abiding values of life; all that is needed is to prepare oneself for them. Utter renouncement is the shortest and surest road to the establishment of one's personality, or more exactly to the accomplishment of what one was born to do.

The love of truth and the search for it for its own sake are the scientific aspects of this abnegation. One must learn to love the truth, irrespective of its use and application—whether it be profitable or not, pleasant or not, encouraging or the opposite. One must forget oneself completely in the presence of and search for truth, and love it in advance whatever it may be. Then only can one find it. This is the main lesson of science. Just as soon as we, as a people, are able to understand it, we shall be truly scientific-minded, and then social justice will be easy enough to accomplish. It is a magnificent prospect, but we have still a long way to go: indeed some of us have just started, and most of us not yet.

Of course our real goal is even more distant, for truth and justice, however necessary, are not sufficient. The purest and sweetest flower of the human heart is charity. In the last analysis there can be no greatness in the human order (as opposed to the order of nature) without magnanimity.

It is surprising that a seed sown in Texel should blossom in Jamaica, for it would be difficult to find two more completely different islands. One is a mere sandbar at the edge of a cold and foggy sea, with but few trees to adorn its bleakness, while the other is set like a jewel in the middle of the Caribbean Sea, its innumerable hills and dales covered with luxuriant vegetation of every clime and kind: pimento trees lending to the landscape a touch of classical beauty, bamboo groves suggesting all the graces of Asia, and other trees and shrubs without number. Yet this was my strange experience: I understood fully only in Jamaica what had been hinted to me in Texel many years before. The strangeness lies merely in the remoteness of the places, otherwise the experience is very common. Indeed it is one of the rules of life. Farmers may complain of the uncertainty of their harvests, but this is regularity itself as compared with the capricious ingathering of spiritual crops. Ideas do germinate but nobody can ever foretell when and where. Cast your bread upon the face of the waters, fling the seed—and I do not say that you will reap (why should you?) but there will be a harvest. One must be prepared to sow widely, generously, to cast much bread upon many waters, and to gather in but little and late if at all. The personality of the reaper is unknown, but the reaping is almost certain. That is enough.

The scientists and scholars who appreciate the history of science to-day are very few in number, but that does not matter very much. The essential is that there be a small body of men who do appreciate it and who try to interpret the human past and present in such terms; they are walking in the right direction and more scientists and scholars will follow them by and by. Selfishness and patience are incompatible because of the brevity of our lives, but just as soon as we forget ourselves either in search of truth or in the evangelical way or preferably in both ways, it is easy enough to be patient. The speed of human progress is less important than its direction. Let us use our best scientific and historic means to determine and to correct that direction; it cannot be determined once and forever, but must be continually corrected as our knowledge and wisdom improve. Then let us follow it as faithfully and as humbly as possible, allowing for the development of whatever gentleness and kindness there may be in us. It is a long way to go, but we should enjoy every step of it.

EDITORIAL NOTE, ACKNOWLEDGMENTS, AND SOURCES

The essays making up this volume have been chosen to give both the general reader and the student a better understanding of the history of science, its scope, purpose, and methods. They have been selected from the author's writings over a period of some thirty years. "East and West in the History of Science" was suggested for inclusion by Professor Henry Guerlac of Cornell. "Casting Bread Upon the Face of the Waters" was suggested by Mrs. George Sarton. The remaining essays were chosen and prepared for publication by Frances Davis Cohen and I. Bernard Cohen.

Although some of these essays have been printed elsewhere, chiefly in scholarly journals of limited circulation, they have not hitherto been available to the reader at large. In reprinting them, no attempt has been made to publish them *verbatim et literatim*. Since they appeared in different places, and at different times, there was a certain amount of repetition which has been eliminated. In one case, selections from two separate essays were combined in order to form an introductory section to Part Two: "Secret History," the title of which derives from an essay which appeared in *Scribner's Magazine*, 1920, 67: 187-192; in other cases, sections primarily of interest to research scholars and scientists, as well as references to contemporaneous matters no longer of immediate concern, have been eliminated; finally, the extensive bibliographic and iconographic footnotes, as well as facsimiles, have been suppressed, since they are of interest only to the specialist. In the list which appears below, all such deletions and emendations are indicated.

Grateful thanks are offered the publishers of the essays listed below for permission to reprint them in this volume.

SOURCES · PART ONE

"The Spread of Understanding" is printed from a hitherto unpublished manuscript of 1922.

"The History of Medicine versus the History of Art" was the Fielding H. Garrison Lecture read before the Seventeenth Annual Meeting of the American Association of the History of Medicine, Atlantic City, N. J., 4-6 May 1941. It first appeared in *Bulletin of the History of Medicine*, 1941, *10*: 123-135, and is reprinted with a few minor emendations, and without the bibliographic footnotes.

"The History of Science" is reprinted with a few deletions and minor emendations from *The Monist*, 1916, *26*: 321-365.

PART TWO

"Secret History" is made up of a portion of "The Teaching of the History of Science," *Isis*, 1921-2, *4*: 225-249 and a portion of "The New Humanism," *Isis*, 1924, *6*: 9-42.

"Leonardo and the Birth of Modern Science" was first published under the title "The Message of Leonardo: His Relation to the Birth of Modern Science," in *Scribner's Magazine*, 1919, *65*: 531-540; it is reprinted here with several deletions and emendations.

"Evariste Galois" was first printed in *The Scientific Monthly*, 1921, *13*: 363-375, and was reprinted in *Osiris*, 1937, *3*: 241-259 (with portrait, facsimiles, and bibliography).

"Ernest Renan" is printed from an original manuscript of 1922; a portion of this essay was printed in *The Nineteenth Century and After*, 1922, *92*: 953-961.

"Herbert Spencer" is an abbreviated form of an essay with the same title in *Scribner's Magazine*, 1920, *67*: 695-701; reprinted in *Isis*, 1921, *3*: 375-390 (with portrait and elaborate biographical and iconographic notes).

PART THREE

"East and West in the History of Science" was originally the second of the Colver Lectures at Brown University for the year 1930, which were printed under the title, *The History of Science and the New Humanism* (first published by Henry Holt and Company, New York, 1930; reprinted by the Harvard University Press, Cambridge, Mass., 1937). The essay as printed here differs from the previously printed version in the omission of several paragraphs and the bibliographic references, and in several minor emendations, including the introduction of a footnote from another section of that book. The title has been enlarged from the original "East and West" to the more suggestive title, "East and West in the History of Science," which was used in the Spanish translation appearing in *Al-Andalus*, 1934, 2: 261-297.

PART FOUR

"An Institute for the History of Science and Civilization" is the author's third article on this subject; the previous two having been published in *Science*, 1917, 45: 284-286; 46: 399-402. The present version was issued in a small mimeographed edition on 5 December 1936, and was published with an introduction and an appendix in *Isis*, 1938, 28: 7-17. It is printed here with a few slight emendations.

"Casting Bread upon the Face of the Waters" is reprinted from *Isis*, 1934, 21: 488-501 with a few deletions and without the bibliographic footnotes.

INDEX